It's another Quality Book from CGP

This book is for anyone doing Cambridge IGCSE Mathematics.

It contains lots of tricky questions designed
to make you sweat — because that's the only
way you'll get any better.

It's also got some daft bits in to try and make
the whole experience at least vaguely
entertaining for you.

What CGP is all about

Our sole aim here at CGP is to produce the highest quality
books — carefully written, immaculately presented and
dangerously close to being funny.

Then we work our socks off to get them out to you
— at the cheapest possible prices.

Contents

Section Five

SHAPES, AREAS AND DRAWING

Section Six

ANGLES AND GEOMETRY

Section Seven

HANDLING DATA

Throughout this book, the more challenging questions are marked with boxes like this: **Q1**

Published by Coordination Group Publications Ltd.
Illustrated by Ruso Bradley, Lex Ward and Ashley Tyson

From original material by Richard Parsons.

Contributors: Gill Allen, JE Dodds, Mark Haslam, C McLoughlin, John Waller, Dave Williams

Updated by: Helena Hayes, Paul Jordin, Sharon Keeley-Holden, Lyn Setchell

With thanks to Mary Falkner and Jane Appleton for the proofreading.

ISBN: 978 1 84762 558 8

Groovy website: www.cgpbooks.co.uk
Printed by Elanders Hindson Ltd, Newcastle upon Tyne.
Jolly bits of clipart from CorelDRAW® and VECTOR.

Types of Number

There are a few special types of number you really need to know about —
including **SQUARE** and **CUBE NUMBERS**, **INTEGERS**, **REAL NUMBERS** and
NATURAL NUMBERS, and **RATIONAL** and **IRRATIONAL NUMBERS**.

Q1   Sarah thinks of a positive number. She calculates that the square of the number is 256. What is the square root of Sarah's number?

Q2   On a certain day the temperature at midday was 14 °C. By midnight the temperature had fallen by 17 °C. What was the temperature at midnight?

Q3   1 is the first odd number. It is also the first square number and the first cube number. Which is greater: the third odd number, the third square number or the third cube number?

Q4   Write down the first four terms of the following sequence:
The squares of odd numbers starting from $9^2 = 81$.

Q5   Write down which of the numbers in the box below are:

   a) Real numbers
   b) Natural numbers
   c) Integers.

17	-4	0	π	9123
3.7	5	-9123	42	85
12.4	-0.3	33	12.00	100 000

Q6   Write down a rational number and an irrational number both greater than $\sqrt{5}$ and less than 5.

Q7   Five of the numbers in the box below
are rational and five are irrational:

$\sqrt{2} \times \sqrt{8}$	$(\sqrt{5})^6$	$\sqrt{3} \div \sqrt{2}$	$(\sqrt{7})^3$	6π
0.4	$\sqrt{5} - 2.1$	$40 - 2^{-1} - 4^{-2}$	$49^{-1/2}$	$\sqrt{6} - 6$

   a) Write down the five rational numbers.
   b) Write down the five irrational numbers.

Multiples, Factors and Primes

Q1   1   3   6   9   12
From the numbers above, write down:
a) a multiple of 4
b) the prime number
c) two square numbers
d) three factors of 27
e) two numbers, P and Q, that satisfy both $P = 2Q$ and $P = \sqrt{144}$

This is real basic stuff —
you just have to know
your times tables. And
your primes, of course...

Q2   A school ran 3 evening classes: Conversational French, Cake Making and Woodturning. The Conversational French class had 29 students, Cake Making had 27 students, and the Woodturning class had 23. For which classes did the teacher have difficulty dividing the students into equal groups?

Q3   a) Write down the first five cube numbers.
b) Which of the numbers given in part a) are multiples of 2?
c) Which of the numbers given in part a) are multiples of 3?
d) Which of the numbers given in part a) are multiples of 4?
e) Which of the numbers given in part a) are multiples of 5?

Q4   Using any or all of the figures **1, 2, 5, 9** write down:
a) the smallest prime number
b) a prime number greater than 20
c) a prime number between 10 and 20
d) two prime numbers whose sum is 21
e) a number that is not prime.

*Remember — 1 is not a prime.
Look, it just isn't, OK.*

Q5   What is the largest prime less than 300?

Q6   How many prime numbers are even?

Q7   Bryan and Sue were playing a guessing game. Sue thought of a number between 1 and 100 which Bryan had to guess. Bryan was allowed to ask five questions, which are listed with Sue's responses in the table below.

Bryan's Questions	Sue's Responses
Is it prime?	No
Is it odd?	No
Is it less than 50?	Yes
Is it a multiple of 3?	Yes
Is it a multiple of 7?	Yes

Start by writing down
a number table up to 100.
Look at each response in
turn and cross off numbers
till you've only got
one left.

What is the number that Sue thought of?

Multiples, Factors and Primes

Top tip These two fancy names always put people off — but really they're dead easy. Just learn these simple facts:

> **1) The Lowest Common Multiple (LCM) is the SMALLEST number that will DIVIDE BY ALL the numbers in question.**
>
> E.g.   3, 6, 9, 12, 15 are all multiples of 3.
> 5, 10, 15, 20, 25 are all multiples of 5.
> The lowest number that is in both lists is 15, so 15 is the LCM of 3 and 5.

> **2) The Highest Common Factor (HCF) is the BIGGEST number that will DIVIDE INTO ALL the numbers in question.**
>
> E.g.   1, 2, 4, 8 are all factors of 8.
> 1, 2, 3, 4, 6, 12 are all factors of 12.
> The highest number that is in both lists is 4, so 4 is the HCF of 8 and 12.

Q8 **a)** List the first ten multiples of 6, starting at 6.
b) List the first ten multiples of 5, starting at 5.
c) What is the LCM of 5 and 6?

I tell you what, it's a lot easier to find the LCM or HCF once you've listed the multiples or factors. If you miss out this step it'll all go horribly wrong, believe me.

Q9 **a)** List all the factors of 30.
b) List all the factors of 48.
c) What is the HCF of 30 and 48?

Q10 For each set of numbers find the HCF.
a) 40, 60	**d)** 15, 45	**g)** 32, 64
b) 10, 40, 60	**e)** 15, 30, 45	**h)** 32, 48, 64
c) 10, 24, 40, 60	**f)** 15, 20, 30, 45	**i)** 16, 32, 48, 64

Q11 For each set of numbers find the LCM.
a) 40, 60	**d)** 15, 45	**g)** 32, 64
b) 10, 40, 60	**e)** 15, 30, 45	**h)** 32, 48, 64
c) 10, 24, 40, 60	**f)** 15, 20, 30, 45	**i)** 16, 32, 48, 64

Q12 Lars, Rita and Alan regularly go swimming. Lars goes every 2 days, Rita goes every 3 days and Alan goes every 5 days. They all went swimming together on Friday 1st June.

This is just a 'Lowest Common Multiple' question in disguise.

a) On what date will Lars and Rita next go swimming together?
b) On what date will Rita and Alan next go swimming together?
c) On what day of the week will all 3 next go swimming together?
d) Which of the 3 (if any) will go swimming on 15th June?

Square and Cube Roots

Square root just means "WHAT NUMBER TIMES ITSELF (i.e. 2×2) GIVES..."
The square roots of 64 are 8 and −8 because 8×8=64 and -8×-8=64.

Cube root means "WHAT NUMBER TIMES ITSELF TWICE (i.e. 2×2×2) GIVES ..."
The cube root of 27 is 3 because 3×3×3=27.

Square roots always have a + and − answer, cube roots only have 1 answer.

Q1 Use the $\sqrt{}$ button on your calculator to find the following <u>positive</u> square roots to the nearest whole number.

  a) $\sqrt{60}$ e) $\sqrt{520}$ i) $\sqrt{170}$

  b) $\sqrt{19}$ f) $\sqrt{75}$ j) $\sqrt{7220}$

  c) $\sqrt{34}$ g) $\sqrt{750}$ k) $\sqrt{1\,000\,050}$

  d) $\sqrt{200}$ h) $\sqrt{0.9}$ l) $\sqrt{27}$

Q2 Without using a calculator, write down both answers to each of the following:

  a) $\sqrt{4}$ d) $\sqrt{49}$ g) $\sqrt{144}$

  b) $\sqrt{16}$ e) $\sqrt{25}$ h) $\sqrt{64}$

  c) $\sqrt{9}$ f) $\sqrt{100}$ i) $\sqrt{81}$

Q3 Use your calculator to find the following:

  a) $\sqrt[3]{4096}$ d) $\sqrt[3]{1\,000\,000}$

  b) $\sqrt[3]{1728}$ e) $\sqrt[3]{1}$

  c) $\sqrt[3]{1331}$ f) $\sqrt[3]{0.125}$

Q4 Without using a calculator, find the value of the following:

  a) $\sqrt[3]{64}$ d) $\sqrt[3]{1000}$

  b) $\sqrt[3]{512}$ e) $\sqrt[3]{216}$

  c) $\sqrt[3]{125}$ f) $\sqrt[3]{8000}$

Q5 Nida is buying a small storage box online. She sees a cube box with a volume of 343 cm³. What is the length of each box edge?

Q6 A farmer is buying fencing to surround a square field of area 3600 m². What length of fencing does he need to buy?

Order of Operations

Nothing weird here. Just a load of sums to do — while you're at it remember BODMAS.
Both Ocelots Demand Myriad Antique Similes. Hang on, that's not right...
Brackets, Other, Division, Multiplication, Addition, Subtraction. That's better.

Q1 Calculate the following. Give your answers to 2 d.p. where necessary.

a) $6 + 4 \div 2$
b) $(6 + 4) \div 2$
c) $(2 \times 6) - (7 \div 3)^2$
d) $2 \times 6 - 7 \div 3^2$
e) $8 \div (9 \times 3^2) - 1$

f) $4 \times 4^2 + (4 \times 4)^2 - (4 \div 4)^3 \div 4^3$
g) $7 \div (6 \div 3) + 2$
h) $10^3 - (-5)^2 + (64 \div 8)$
i) $(3 \times 3) + 24 \div (2 - 14)^2$
j) $11 \times (77 \div 7) + 121 - 2 \times (10 + 1)^2$

Q2 Calculate the following. Give your answers to 2 d.p. where necessary.

a) $10 + \sqrt{16} - (42 \div 7)$
b) $\sqrt{36} \div 2 + (5 \times 14)$
c) $91 + (\sqrt{289} \times 2) - 12$
d) $\sqrt{1} \times 42 \div 6$
e) $2 + (\sqrt{81} + 3)^2 \div 7$

f) $(\sqrt{400} - 18)^3 + (4 \div 6)$
g) $\sqrt{9} \div 3 \times 2 - 1$
h) $\sqrt{7} + \sqrt{5} - (\sqrt{3} \times 2)$
i) $\sqrt{626} - (4 + 56 \div 3)^2$
j) $(12 - \sqrt{4912}) \div 15^2$

Q3 Calculate the following. Give your answers to 2 d.p. where necessary.

a) $\dfrac{21}{2 + 5}$

b) $\dfrac{3^2}{9 + 9^2}$

c) $\dfrac{\sqrt{16}}{3 \div 12}$

d) $\dfrac{5^2}{\sqrt{49} - 4}$

e) $\dfrac{1 - \sqrt{17}}{\sqrt{45} + 22^2}$

f) $\dfrac{18^2}{2 + \sqrt[3]{17}}$

g) $\dfrac{15^2 - 2^3}{\sqrt{12} - \sqrt{22}}$

h) $\dfrac{4 \times \sqrt[3]{3}}{24 + \sqrt[3]{30}}$

i) $\dfrac{14 + (3 \div 7)}{(3^3 - \sqrt{5})}$

j) $\dfrac{\sqrt[3]{177} - \sqrt{2}}{\sqrt{15} \times 4}$

k) $\dfrac{\sqrt{(81 \div 4)}}{7^3 - (31 \times 0.3)}$

l) $\sqrt{\dfrac{7}{4^3}} - (53 \div 2^4)^2$

6

Calculator Buttons

Q1 Using the x^2 button on your calculator, work out:

a) 1^2
b) 2^2
c) 11^2

d) 16^2
e) $(-1)^2$
f) 30^2

g) $(-5)^2$
h) 1000^2
i) 0^2

Q2 Using the $\sqrt{}$ button on your calculator, work out the following. Give your answers to 2 d.p. where necessary.

a) $\sqrt{16}$
b) $\sqrt{36}$
c) $\sqrt{289}$

d) $\sqrt{0}$
e) $\sqrt{3600}$
f) $\sqrt{400}$

g) $\sqrt{3}$
h) $\sqrt{7}$
i) $\sqrt{30}$

Q3 Use the $\sqrt[3]{}$ button on your calculator to work out:

a) $\sqrt[3]{1}$
b) $\sqrt[3]{0}$
c) $\sqrt[3]{343}$
d) $\sqrt[3]{1000}$

e) $\sqrt[3]{27}$
f) $\sqrt[3]{-27}$
g) $\sqrt[3]{-64}$
h) $\sqrt[3]{-5}$

Yeah, OK, we all know how to do sums on a calculator — but it can do so much more... check out the groovy powers button and the funky brackets buttons, not to mention the slinky $1/x$ button...

Q4 By calculating the bottom line (the denominator) first and storing it in your calculator, work out:

a) $\dfrac{21}{2 + \sin 30°}$

b) $\dfrac{\tan 15°}{12 + 12^2}$

c) $\dfrac{15}{\cos 30° + 22}$

d) $\dfrac{18}{3 + \sqrt[3]{12}}$

e) $\dfrac{12}{12 + \tan 60°}$

f) $\dfrac{18}{11 + \tan 77°}$

Q5 Using the $a\frac{b}{c}$ button on your calculator:

a) reduce to the lowest terms: i) $\dfrac{3}{9}$ ii) $\dfrac{56}{91}$ iii) $\dfrac{512}{4096}$

b) convert to mixed fractions: i) $\dfrac{17}{5}$ ii) $\dfrac{223}{24}$ iii) $\dfrac{9658}{214}$

c) convert to top-heavy fractions: i) $2\frac{1}{3}$ ii) $8\frac{11}{23}$ iii) $41\frac{52}{63}$

Section One — Numbers

Calculator Buttons

Q6 Using and [---)], calculate:

a) $\dfrac{(14 + 18)}{(2 \times 8)}$

c) $\dfrac{(9 + (4 \div 2))}{(11 \times 3)}$

e) $\dfrac{12}{(8 + 9)(13 - 11)}$

b) $\dfrac{8}{(1 \times 4)(8 - 6)}$

d) $\dfrac{14(4 \times 8)}{(6 + 9)}$

f) $\dfrac{7(5 + 4)}{12(9 \times 8)}$

Q7 Using the X^y or ∧ button, find:

a) 2^0

b) 4^{10}

c) 2^{20}

d) π^2

e) 2^{-1}

f) 3^{10}

g) $(\cos 30°)^5$

h) 4.29^7

i) $(\sin 45°)^4$

For entering numbers into your calculator in standard form you need the **EXP** or **EE** button. It actually means $\times 10^n$ so be careful not to type in the $\times 10$ part.

E.g. to enter 3.4×10^5 you would only need to type **3** **•** **4** **EXP** **5** **=** and <u>not</u> **3** **•** **4** **×** **10** **EXP** **5** **=**

Q8 Enter the following numbers into your calculator and write down what you get:

a) 4×10^3

b) 1×10^4

c) 6.2×10^5

Q9 Work out:

a) $\dfrac{2 \times 10^2}{5 \times 10^1}$

d) $\dfrac{2.3 \times 10^5}{4.6 \times 10^6}$

b) $\dfrac{4.2 \times 10^4}{2.1 \times 10^5}$

e) $\dfrac{7.0 \times 10^3}{3.5 \times 10^5}$

c) $\dfrac{1.92 \times 10^3}{9.6 \times 10^2}$

f) $\dfrac{4.44 \times 10^4}{1.11 \times 10^2}$

Standard Form

Writing very big (or very small) numbers gets a bit messy with all those zeros if you don't use standard form. But of course, the main reason for knowing about standard form is... you guessed it — it's in the Exam.

Q1   Delilah is doing some calculations for her science homework but her calculator is stuck on 'standard form' mode. She needs to give her answers as ordinary numbers. How should she write the following answers?

a) 3.56×10

b) 3.56×10^3

c) 3.56×10^{-1}

d) 3.56×10^4

e) 0.082×10^2

f) 0.082×10^{-2}

g) 0.082×10

h) 0.082×10^{-1}

i) 157×10

j) 157×10^{-3}

k) 157×10^3

l) 157×10^{-1}

Q2   Write in standard form:

a) 2.56

b) 25.6

c) 0.256

d) 25 600

e) 95.2

f) 0.0952

g) 95 200

h) 0.000952

i) 4200

j) 0.0042

k) 42

l) 420

Q3   Write in standard form:

a) 34.7×10

b) 73.004

c) 0.005×10^3

d) 9183×10^2

e) 15 million

f) 937.1×10^4

g) 0.000075

h) 0.05×10^{-2}

i) 534×10^{-2}

j) 621.03

k) 149×10^2

l) 0.003×10^{-4}

Q4   When scientists write about massive things such as the universe, or tiny things such as cells and particles, it's often more convenient to write numbers in standard form. Write the numbers in parts a) to e) in standard form.

a) The average diameter of a cell nucleus in a mammal is around 0.006 mm.

b) A billion = a thousand million.

c) A trillion = a thousand billion.

d) A light year is 9 460 000 000 000 km (approx).

e) Nautilus covered 69 138 miles before having to refuel.

Q5   A tissue sample is three cells thick. Each cell has a thickness of 0.000004 m. What is the thickness of the tissue sample, in mm? Give your answer in standard form.

Q6   This table gives the diameter and distance from the Sun of some planets.

Planet	Distance from Sun (km)	Diameter (km)
Earth	1.5×10^8	1.3×10^4
Venus	1.085×10^8	1.2×10^4
Mars	2.28×10^8	6.8×10^3
Mercury	5.81×10^7	4.9×10^3
Jupiter	7.8×10^8	1.4×10^5
Neptune	4.52×10^9	4.9×10^4
Saturn	1.43×10^9	1.2×10^5

From the table write down which planet is:

a) smallest in diameter

b) largest in diameter

c) nearest to the Sun

d) furthest from the Sun.

Write down which planets are:

e) nearer to the Sun than the Earth

f) bigger in diameter than the Earth.

Standard Form

This stuff gets a lot easier if you know how to handle your calculator.

Q7   If $x = 4 \times 10^5$ and $y = 6 \times 10^4$ work out the value of
a) xy **b)** $4x$ **c)** $3y$.

Q8   Which is <u>greater</u>, 4.62×10^{12} or 1.04×10^{13}, and <u>by how much</u>?

Q9   Which is <u>smaller</u> 3.2×10^{-8} or 1.3×10^{-9} and by how much?

Q10   The following numbers are <u>not</u> written in standard form.
Rewrite them correctly using standard form.

a) 42×10^6 **d)** 11.2×10^{-5} **g)** 17×10^{17}
b) 38×10^{-5} **e)** 843×10^3 **h)** 28.3×10^{-5}
c) 10×10^6 **f)** 42.32×10^{-4} **i)** 10×10^{-3}

> **Don't forget** — when you're using a calculator, you've got to write the answer as **3.46 × 10²⁷**, <u>not</u> as **3.46²⁷**. If you do it the wrong way, it means something <u>completely</u> different.

Q11   What is <u>7 million</u> in standard form?

Q12   The radius of the Earth is 6.38×10^3 km. What is the radius of the Earth measured in <u>cm</u>? Give your answer in standard form.

Q13   One atomic mass unit is equivalent to 1.661×10^{-27} kg.
What are <u>two</u> atomic mass units equivalent to (in standard form)?

Q14   The length of a light year, the distance light can travel in one year, is 9.461×10^{15} m.
How far can light travel in
a) 2 years?
b) 6 months?
Write your answers in <u>standard form</u>.

Q15 a) The surface area of the Earth is approximately 5.1×10^8 km². Write this <u>without</u> using standard form.
b) The area of the Earth covered by sea is 362 000 000 km². Write this in standard form.
c) What is the approximate area of the Earth covered by land? Write your answer <u>without</u> using standard form.

Sets

Sets aren't scary — all they are is collections of things. Now you just have to show how these things relate to each other. There are diagrams to draw and symbols to learn. Fortunately, here's some questions to practice with...

Q1   The elements of set E are all the prime numbers less than 12.
 a) Write set E as a rule using set notation.
 b) Write set E as a complete list of its elements.

Q2   H = {1, 4, 9, 16, 20, 36, 49, 64, 81, 100}
 K = {Integers}
 L = {Natural numbers ≤ 0}
 a) Which one of these sets = ∅
 b) What does n(H) equal?
 c) Write down a number that is an element of set K and one that is not an element of set K using set notation.

Q3   Set B is shown in the Venn diagram below:

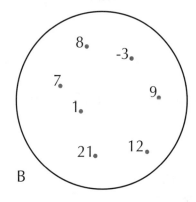

 a) Write set B as a complete list of its elements.
 b) Set C = {odd numbers between 18 and 34}. Draw a Venn diagram of set C.

Q4   Using the Venn diagram on the right find:
 a) Set R as a list of its elements
 b) n(S)
 c) Set R ∩ S
 d) n(R ∪ S)

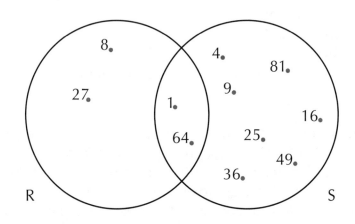

Sets

Q5 This Venn diagram shows the results of a survey about revision. Set D shows those people who listen to dolphins and set P those who take advice from peacocks.

a) What does the universal set, ξ, represent in this diagram?

b) How many people don't take revision advice from dolphins or peacocks?

c) Find n(D ∪ P) and n(D ∩ P)

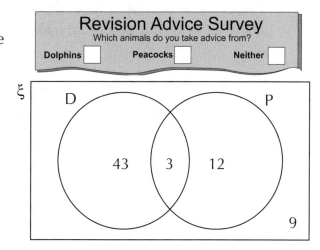

Q6 Draw Venn diagrams for:

a) A = {odd natural numbers less than 20} and B = {prime numbers less than 20}

b) C = {integers greater than or equal to -4 and less than or equal to 4} and D = {natural numbers less than 5}

Q7 A = {x: 0 ≤ x ≤ 18}   B = {y: y is a multiple of 3}   C = {z: z is a factor of 15}

Say whether each of the following statements about sets A, B and C are true or false.

a) 0 ∉ A

b) 0 ∈ C

c) $\frac{2}{3}$ ∈ A

d) B ⊂ A

e) A ⊆ C

f) C ⊂ B

g) C ⊂ A

h) {6} ∈ B

i) {6} ⊆ B

j) 6 ⊂ B

k) (B ∩ C) ⊂ A

l) (B ∪ C) ⊂ A

Q8 John travels around Milton Keynes and counts different types of cows. In addition to real cows he finds artificial cows made from different materials and some made from a combination of materials. He records his findings in sets — Concrete (C), Glass (G) and Plastic (P).

a) What is John's universal set?

b) How many real cows did he find?

c) Find n(P)

d) Find n(C ∪ G)

e) Find n(C')

f) Find n(C ∩ P)

g) Find n(C ∩ G ∩ P)

h) How many cows are made from both glass and plastic but not concrete? Write your answer in set notation.

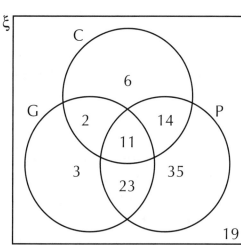

SECTION TWO — MORE NUMBERS

Fractions, Decimals and Percentages

I reckon that converting decimals to percentages is about as easy as it gets — so make the most of it.

Q1 Express each of the following as a percentage:

a) 0.25   c) 0.75   e) 0.4152   g) 0.3962

b) 0.5   d) 0.1   f) 0.8406   h) 0.2828

All you're doing is multiplying by 100 — it really couldn't be easier.

Q2 Express each percentage as a decimal:

a) 50%   c) 40%   e) 60.2%   g) 43.1%

b) 12%   d) 34%   f) 54.9%   h) 78.8%

Now you're dividing by 100 — so just move the decimal point to the left.

Q3 Express each of the following as a percentage:

a) $\dfrac{1}{2}$ e) $\dfrac{1}{25}$

b) $\dfrac{1}{4}$ f) $\dfrac{2}{3}$

c) $\dfrac{1}{8}$ g) $\dfrac{4}{15}$

d) $\dfrac{3}{4}$ h) $\dfrac{2}{7}$

Q4 Express each percentage as a fraction in its lowest terms:

a) 25%   e) 8.2%

b) 60%   f) 49.6%

c) 45%   g) 88.6%

d) 30%   h) 32.4%

Best thing to do with e)-h) is to put them over 100, then get rid of the decimal point by multiplying top and bottom by 10. Then just cancel down as normal.

Q5 119 out of 140 houses on an estate have DVD players. What percentage is this?

Q6 In an exam Tina scored 52/80. The grade she receives depends on the percentage scored. What grade will Tina get?

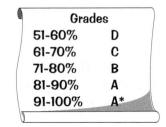

Grades	
51-60%	D
61-70%	C
71-80%	B
81-90%	A
91-100%	A*

Fractions, Decimals and Percentages

 <u>Decimals</u> are just another way of writing <u>fractions</u> —
so it's easy to convert between the two...

Q7   Without using a calculator, write the following fractions as decimals:

a) $\dfrac{3}{10}$ c) $\dfrac{2}{5}$ e) $\dfrac{14}{8}$ g) $\dfrac{24}{40}$

b) $\dfrac{37}{100}$ d) $\dfrac{3}{8}$ f) $\dfrac{8}{64}$ h) $\dfrac{4}{80}$

Q8   Fill in the gaps in the following conversion table :

Fraction	Decimal
½	0.5
⅕	
	0.125
	1.6
⁴⁄16	
⁷⁄2	
	0.x
ˣ⁄100	
³⁄20	
	0.45

Q9   Write the following fractions as recurring decimals:

a) $\dfrac{5}{6}$ c) $\dfrac{7}{11}$ e) $\dfrac{10}{11}$ g) $\dfrac{478}{999}$

b) $\dfrac{7}{9}$ d) $\dfrac{47}{99}$ f) $\dfrac{29}{63}$ h) $\dfrac{5891}{9999}$

Q10   Write the following decimals as fractions in their lowest terms:

a) 0.6   c) 0.95   e) $0.\dot{3}$ g) $0.\dot{1}$

b) 0.75   d) 0.128   f) $0.\dot{6}$ h) $0.1\dot{6}$

A dot over the number means that it's <u>recurring</u>
— so $0.\dot{3}$ = 0.33333333... and so on, forever.

Q11   Write the following recurring decimals as fractions in their lowest terms:

a) 0.222...   c) 0.888...   e) 0.121212...   g) 0.753753753...

b) 0.444...   d) 0.808080...   f) 0.545545545...   h) 0.156156156...

Fractions

Answer the following questions without using a calculator.

Q1 Carry out the following multiplications, giving your answers in their lowest terms:

a) $\dfrac{1}{8} \times \dfrac{1}{8}$

c) $\dfrac{3}{18} \times \dfrac{1}{3}$

e) $1\dfrac{1}{4} \times 4\dfrac{1}{8}$

b) $\dfrac{2}{3} \times \dfrac{1}{6}$

d) $1\dfrac{1}{4} \times 3\dfrac{1}{8}$

f) $\dfrac{9}{10} \times \dfrac{9}{100} \times \dfrac{1}{100}$

Q2 Carry out the following divisions, giving your answers in their lowest terms:

a) $\dfrac{1}{8} \div \dfrac{1}{8}$

c) $\dfrac{3}{18} \div \dfrac{1}{3}$

e) $1\dfrac{1}{4} \div 4\dfrac{1}{8}$

b) $\dfrac{2}{3} \div \dfrac{1}{6}$

d) $1\dfrac{1}{4} \div 3\dfrac{1}{8}$

f) $\left(\dfrac{9}{10} \div \dfrac{9}{100}\right) \div \dfrac{1}{100}$

Q3 Evaluate the following, giving your answers in their lowest terms:

a) $\dfrac{1}{8} + \dfrac{1}{8}$

c) $\dfrac{3}{18} + \dfrac{1}{3}$

e) $1\dfrac{1}{4} + 4\dfrac{1}{8}$

b) $\dfrac{1}{6} + \dfrac{2}{3}$

d) $1\dfrac{1}{4} + 3\dfrac{1}{8}$

f) $\dfrac{9}{10} + \dfrac{9}{100} + \dfrac{1}{100}$

Q4 Caley is making some punch for her birthday party. She mixes $\dfrac{1}{2}$ litre of cranberry juice, $1\dfrac{1}{2}$ litres of apple juice, $\dfrac{2}{3}$ litre of orange juice and $\dfrac{4}{5}$ litres of pineapple juice.

She has a bowl that will hold 4 litres. Will this be big enough to contain all of the punch?

Q5 Evaluate the following, giving your answers in their lowest terms:

a) $\dfrac{1}{8} - \dfrac{1}{8}$

c) $\dfrac{3}{18} - \dfrac{1}{3}$

e) $1\dfrac{1}{8} - 4\dfrac{1}{4}$

b) $\dfrac{2}{3} - \dfrac{1}{6}$

d) $3\dfrac{1}{8} - 1\dfrac{1}{4}$

f) $\left(\dfrac{9}{10} - \dfrac{9}{100}\right) - \dfrac{1}{100}$

Q6 Evaluate the following, giving your answers in their lowest terms:

a) $\dfrac{1}{2} + \dfrac{1}{4}$

e) $6 \times \dfrac{2}{3}$

i) $3 + \dfrac{8}{5}$

b) $\dfrac{2}{3} - \dfrac{1}{4}$

f) $\dfrac{4}{5} \div \dfrac{2}{3}$

j) $\dfrac{2}{3}\left(\dfrac{3}{4} + \dfrac{4}{5}\right)$

c) $\dfrac{1}{5} + \dfrac{2}{3} - \dfrac{2}{5}$

g) $\dfrac{5}{12} \times \dfrac{3}{2}$

k) $\left(\dfrac{1}{7} + \dfrac{3}{14}\right) \times \left(3 - \dfrac{1}{5}\right)$

d) $5 - \dfrac{1}{4}$

h) $\dfrac{5}{6} - \dfrac{7}{8}$

l) $\left(\dfrac{3}{4} - \dfrac{1}{5}\right) \div \left(\dfrac{7}{8} + \dfrac{1}{16}\right)$

Fractions

With long wordy questions you have to pick out the important bits and then translate them into numbers. It's not that easy at first, but you'll get better — I guess you've just gotta learn to ignore the waffly stuff.

Answer these without using your calculator:

Q7 What fraction of 1 hour is:
  a) 5 minutes
  b) 15 minutes
  c) 40 minutes?

Q8 If a TV programme lasts 40 minutes, what fraction of the programme is left after:
  a) 10 minutes
  b) 15 minutes
  c) 35 minutes?

Q9 A café employs eighteen girls and twelve boys to wait at tables. Another six boys and nine girls work in the kitchen.
What fraction of the <u>kitchen staff</u> are girls?
What fraction of the <u>employees</u> are boys?

Q10

In a survey, people were asked if they liked a new cola drink. One in five thought it was great, four out of fifteen felt there was no difference in taste, three in ten disliked it and <u>the rest</u> offered no opinion.
What fraction of people offered no opinion?

Q11 Neil wore red trousers on a total of 12 days in November.
  a) On what fraction of the total number of days in November did Neil wear <u>red trousers</u>?
  b) For 1/5 of the days in November Neil wore a <u>blue shirt</u>. How many days is this?

Q12

The Sandwich Club of Great Britain are going on their annual picnic.
  a) The boxes they use to transport their sandwiches are 10 inches high and are the width and length of a single sandwich. Each sandwich is 5/8 of an inch thick. How many boxes will they need for 80 sandwiches?
  b) How tall would the box need to be if <u>40</u> sandwiches were to be stacked inside?

Fractions

You can use your calculator for these questions.

Q13 The population of Australia is 18 million, of which 3.5 million people live in Sydney and 1 million people live in Perth.

This stuff is pretty easy — but you don't want to make silly mistakes in the exam. Get the practice in now.

   a) What fraction of the population live in Perth?

   b) What fraction of the population live in Perth or Sydney?

Q14 Green Island is split into six regions A, B, C, D, E and F.
The areas of the six regions are 12, 2, 3, 18, 4, and 9 km² respectively.

   a) What is the total area of the island?

   b) What fraction of the island's area is taken up by the two largest regions?

Q15 In a consumer survey, 100 people stated their favourite vegetable.
25 people chose peas, 35 carrots and 32 spinach.

   a) How many of the 100 people chose a vegetable other than peas, carrots or spinach?

   b) What fraction of the 100 people chose carrots as their favourite vegetable?

   c) What fraction of the 100 people chose peas as their favourite vegetable?

   d) At least how many people chose a green vegetable as their favourite?

   e) Not more than how many people chose a green vegetable as their favourite?

Q16 A ball is dropped from a height of 6 m.

6m

After each bounce the ball rises to 2/3 of its previous height. What height will it reach after the third bounce?

Q17 George wants to make a cake. The recipe requires 150 g each of flour, sugar and butter, and 3 eggs. George only has 2 eggs so he decides to make a smaller cake with the same proportions.

   a) How much flour will George need to use?

   b) If each egg weighs 25 g, how much will the cake weigh before it goes in the oven?

   c) What fraction of the uncooked weight is flour?

   d) If the cake loses 1/7 of its weight during baking (due to moisture loss) what will it weigh after baking?

Q18 Jenny goes shopping. She gets 1/3 off a bag priced £28, 1/5 off a dress priced £62 and 2/3 off a hat priced £14. How much money does she save?

Multiplying and Dividing Decimals

Some simple rules to help you out here — do <u>multiplication</u> as if the numbers were whole numbers and sort out the decimal points <u>afterwards</u>, do <u>division</u> just as you would with whole numbers, but make sure you <u>line up</u> the decimal points.

Do these questions without using a calculator.

Q1 Multiply the following decimals:
a) 2.1 × 1.2
b) 3.8 × 4.5
c) 9.3 × 3.9
d) 2.5 × 11.4
e) 15.6 × 5.7
f) 7.1 × 14.3
g) 18.2 × 20.3
h) 210.2 × 120.1

Q2 Divide the following decimals:
a) 92.4 ÷ 0.4
b) 12.8 ÷ 0.2
c) 62.4 ÷ 1.6
d) 0.4 ÷ 0.8
e) 88.8 ÷ 11.1
f) 101.6 ÷ 3.2
g) 0.23 ÷ 0.04
h) 156.3 ÷ 208.4

Q3 A group of friends went out for a meal together.
The total bill was €73.80 and each person paid €12.30.
a) How many people were there at the meal?
b) Drinks made up 20% of the cost of each meal.
How much did drinks cost each person?

Q4 Josephine is baking a cake. She finds a recipe that makes enough cake for 24 people. The table below show the ingredients and quantities required.
a) There are 18 people coming to her party. Use the table to calculate how much of each ingredient she needs to make a cake for 18 people.
b) Calculate the total cost of the ingredients for the cake.

Ingredient	Amount	Cost
Sugar	1.2 kg	£1.50 / kg
Butter	1.2 kg	£4.40 / kg
Flour	1.4 kg	£1.20 / kg
Eggs	20	£2.72 / 12
Milk	0.16 l	£0.84 / l
Vanilla	0.03 l	1.20/ 50 ml

=

Note: stand not included

Q5 Erno is watching the Olympics:
a) A hurdler runs 110 m in 13.4 s. What is his average speed?
b) A discus travels 68.4 m with an average speed of 36 m/s. How long does it fly for?
c) An archer shoots an arrow which travels at an average speed of 61.25 m/s. It takes 0.8 s to reach the target. How far does it travel in flight?
d) A gymnast receives the following scores:

Canada	Mexico	Estonia	Ghana	Brunei	Iceland
5.2	4.9	5.0	5.1	5.3	5.1

What is the gymnast's average score?

See the next page for more about speed, distance and time.

Speed, Distance and Time

This is an easy enough formula — and of course you can put it in that good old formula triangle as well.

$$\text{Average speed} = \frac{\text{Total distance}}{\text{Total time}}$$

Q1   A train travels 240 km in 4 hours. What is its <u>average speed</u>?

Q2   A car travels for 3 hours at an average speed of 55 km/h. How far has it travelled?

Q3   A boy rides a bike at an average speed of 15 km/h. How long will it take him to ride 40 km?

Q4   <u>Complete</u> this table.

Distance Travelled	Time Taken	Average Speed
210 km	3 hrs	
135 km		30 km/h
	2 hrs 30 mins	42 km/h
9 km	45 mins	
640 km		800 km/h
	1 hr 10 mins	60 km/h

Q5   An athlete can run 100 m in 11 seconds.
Calculate the athlete's speed in:
  a) m/s
  b) km/h.

Q6   A plane flies over city A at 09.55 and over city B at 10.02.
What is its <u>average</u> speed if these cities are 63 km apart? Give your answer in km/h.

Q7   The distance from Kendal (Oxenholme) to London (Euston) is 420 km. The train travels at an average speed of 115 km/h. Pete needs to be in London by 10.30. If he catches the 07.05 from Kendal, will he be in London on time? <u>Show all your working</u>.

Q8   In a speed trial a sand yacht travelled a measured kilometre in 36.4 seconds.
  a) Calculate this speed in km/h.
On the return kilometre it took 36.16 seconds.
  b) Find the <u>total time</u> for the two runs.
  c) Calculate the average speed of the two runs in km/h.

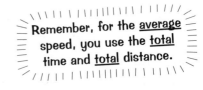

Remember, for the <u>average</u> speed, you use the <u>total</u> time and <u>total</u> distance.

Q9   A motorist drives from Manchester to London. 290 km is on motorway where he averages 100 km/h. 90 km is on city roads where he averages 45 km/h, 25 km is on country roads where he averages 40 km/h.
  a) Calculate the total time taken for the journey.
  b) How far did he travel altogether?
  c) Calculate the average speed for the journey.

Speed, Distance and Time

Q10   Victor walks at an average speed of 4 km/h. He needs to walk to Askam-in-Furness,
3 km away. He needs to be there at 3.00pm. What time should he set off?

Q11   The distance between two railway stations is 145 km.
    a) How long does a train travelling at 65 km/h on average take to travel this distance?
    b) Another train travels on a parallel track at an average speed of 80 km/h, but has a
10 min stop during the journey. How long does this second train take?
    c) If both arrive at 1600, what time did each leave?

Q12   Two athletes ran a road race. One ran at an average speed of 16 km/h, the other
at 4 m/s. Which was the fastest? How long would each take to run 10 km?

Q13   A plane leaves Amsterdam at 0715 and flies at an average speed of 650 km/h to Paris,
arriving at 0800. It takes off again at 0840 and flies at the same average speed to Nice
arriving at 1005.
    a) How far is it from Amsterdam to Paris?
    b) How far is it from Paris to Nice?
    c) What was the average speed for the whole journey?

Q14   A runner covered the first 100 m of a 200 m race in 12.3 seconds.
    a) What was his average speed for the first 100 m?
    b) The second 100 m took 15.1 seconds. What was his average speed for the 200 m?

Q15   A military plane can achieve a speed of 1100 km/h. At this speed it
passes over town A at 1205 and town B at 1217.
    a) How far apart are towns A and B?
    b) The plane then flies over village C which is 93 km from B.
How long does it take to get from B to C?

Q16   Two cars set off on 290 km journeys. One manages an average speed of 68 km/h.
The other car achieves an average speed of 103 km/h when the car is moving, but the
driver stops for a break. If they both take the same time over the journey, for how long
does the second car stop?

Q17   A stone is dropped from a cliff top. After 1 second it has fallen
4.8 m, after 2 seconds a total of 19.2 m and after 3 seconds
43.2 m. Calculate its average speed:
    a) in the first second
    b) in the second second
    c) for all 3 seconds
    d) Change all the m/s speeds to km/h.

Q18   Three racing drivers recorded average speeds of 236.6, 233.8 and 227.3 km/h.
If 1 km = 0.62 miles, how long in seconds would each driver take to travel
5 miles at these speeds?

SECTION TWO — MORE NUMBERS

Ratios

I don't want to spoil the surprise, but you're going to need your calculator for some of these questions — get your finger on that fraction button...

RATIOS are like FRACTIONS which are like DECIMALS

We can treat the RATIO 3:4 like the FRACTION ¾, which is 0.75 as a DECIMAL.

Watch out though — this <u>isn't</u> ¾ of the <u>total</u>:
If there are girls and boys in the ratio **3:4**, it means there are ¾ as many girls as boys.
So if there are **8 boys**, there are **¾ × 8 = 6 girls.**

Q1 Write these ratios in their simplest forms:
a) 6:8 **c)** 1.5:3 **e)** 2 weeks:4 days
b) 5:20 **d)** 2¼:4 **f)** £1.26:14p

Q2 A rectangle has sides in the ratio 1:2. Calculate the length of the longer side if the shorter side is:

a) 3 cm **b)** 5.5 cm **c)** 15.2 m

Calculate the length of the shorter side if the longer side is:

d) 3 cm **e)** 5.5 cm **f)** 15.2 m

Q3 Divide the following amounts in the ratios given:
a) £20 in the ratio 2:3 **c)** 500 g in the ratio 1:2:2
b) 150 m in the ratio 8:7 **d)** 8 hrs in the ratio 1:2:3

For these you add up the ratio numbers to find the total number of parts and <u>divide</u> by this. Then <u>multiply</u> by each number in the ratio separately to find the different amounts.

Q4 John and Peter share a bar of chocolate marked into 16 squares.
They share it in the ratio 1:3 respectively. How many squares does each boy get?

Q5 A 2 litre bottle of cola is to be shared between three girls in the ratio 2:3:5. How many <u>millilitres</u> will each girl get?

<u>Watch out for your units</u> — you'll have to change them over for this one — and your answer should be in <u>millilitres</u>.

Q6 Tony gives £100 to be shared by Jane, Holly and Rose in a ratio according to their <u>age</u>. Jane is 10, Holly is 12 and Rose is 3 years old. How much will each child get?

Q7 Sunil and Paul work in a restaurant. As they work different hours, they split their tips in the ratio 3:4. One night they got £28 in tips between them. Who got the most money from the tips and how much did they get?

Q8 The recipe for flapjacks is 250 g of oats, 150 g of brown sugar and 100 g of margarine. What <u>fraction of the mixture</u> is:
a) oats? **b)** sugar?

Q9 The ratio of girls to boys in a school is 7:6. If there are 455 pupils in total, how many are
a) girls? **b)** boys?

Ratios

Q10 **a)** Luke and Miranda split a pizza. They split the cost in the ratio 2:3.
Luke pays £3.20. If Miranda pays more, how much does she pay?

b) A rectangular bookcase is 120 cm long. The length is in a ratio of 3:2 to the height.
What is the height of this bookcase?

Q11 Oak and ash saplings are planted along a roadside in the ratio 2:3 respectively.
If there are 20 oak saplings, how many ash saplings are there?

Q12 Sarah works as a waitress. Each week, she splits her wage into spending money
and savings in the ratio 7:3.

a) One week, Sarah earns £130.
How much should she put in her savings that week?

b) The next week, Sarah put £42 into her savings.
How much did she earn in total that week?

Q13 An architect is drawing the plan of a house to a scale of
1 cm to 3 m.

Make sure you convert to the same units when you're working out the ratio.

a) Write this ratio in its simplest form.

b) How wide is a room that appears as 2 cm on the drawing?

c) The hall is 1000 cm long. How long will the architect need
to make it on the drawing?

Q14 Concrete is mixed using cement, sand and gravel in the ratio
1:3:6. If Dave uses a 5000 g bag of cement, how much:

a) sand does he need?

b) gravel does he need?

c) If Dave needs 80 kg of concrete,
how much of each substance does he need?

Q15

I picked some strawberries after a few wet days.
Some were nibbled by snails, some were mouldy
and some fine. The ratio was 2:3:10 respectively.
If <u>9 strawberries were mouldy</u> how many:

a) were fine?

b) were not fine?

c) What fraction of the total amount were fine?

Q16 Salt & Vinegar, Cheese & Onion and
Prawn Cocktail flavour crisps were sold
in the school tuck shop in <u>the ratio
5:3:2</u>. If 18 bags of Prawn Cocktail
were sold, how many bags:

a) of Salt & Vinegar were sold?

b) were sold altogether?

Proportion

Q1   If 3 minibuses can carry 51 students how many students can 5 minibuses carry?

Q2   If 17 textbooks cost £150.45, how much will 28 cost?

Q3   If it takes 4 people 28 hours to complete a task, how long would it take just one person?

Q4   A person earns £6.20 an hour. How much do they earn for 15½ hours work?

Q5   Wool from 8 sheep is needed to make a scarf. How many are needed to knit 12 scarves?

Q6   On a map, 2 cm represents 3 km.
   a) If two towns are 14 km apart, what is the distance between them on the map?
   b) If two road junctions are 20.3 cm apart on the map, what is their real distance apart?

Q7   A herd of 7 cows produces 161 litres of milk a day.
         Find the smallest number of cows it would take to
         produce at least 1000 litres per day.

Q8   The number of people who have their hearing damaged at a concert is proportional to
         how loud it is. 480 people have their hearing damaged when the volume is set at '6'.
         How many people suffer hearing damage when:
   a) the volume is set at '4'?
   b) the volume is set at '7'?
   c) the volume is turned up to '11'?

Q9   A scientist proposes that rainfall is proportional to latitude.
         It rains an average of 53.1 cm a year in Milton Keynes
         which is at latitude 52.0° N. If the scientist is correct,
         what is the average rainfall in:
   a) Ulverston — latitude 54.2° N?
   b) Boscastle — latitude 50.4° N?
         If average daytime temperature in July is inversely
         proportional to latitude and it's 21.0°C in Boscastle,
         what will the average daytime temperature in July be in:
   c) Milton Keynes?
   d) Ulverston?

Q10   The speed of light is inversely proportional to the
         refractive index of the material it's travelling through.
         The speed of light in water is 225 000 km/s. Water has a refractive index of 1.33.
         What is the speed of light in:
   a) Glass which has a refractive index of 1.50?
   b) Diamond which has a refractive index of 2.42?
   c) A vacuum which has a refractive index of 1.00?

Percentages

Make sure you can switch from fractions to decimals to percentages before you start.

Q1 Express each percentage as a decimal:

a) 20%   **b)** 35%   **c)** 2%   **d)** 62.5%

Q2 Express each percentage as a fraction in its lowest terms:

a) 20%   **b)** 3%   **c)** 70%   **d)** 84.2%

Q3 Express each of the following as a percentage:

a) $\dfrac{1}{8}$ **b)** 0.23   **c)** $\dfrac{12}{40}$ **d)** 0.34

Q4 In a French test, Lauren scored 17/20. What percentage is this?

Q5 87 out of 120 pupils at Backwater School have access to a computer.
What percentage is this?

There are three types of percentage question. The first one is working out "something % of something else" — it's dead easy. Just remember to add it back on to the original amount if you've got a VAT question.

Q6 John bought a new TV. The tag in the shop said it cost £299 + VAT.
If VAT is charged at 17½%, how much did he pay (to the nearest penny)?

Q7 Four friends stay at the Pickled Parrot Hotel for a night and each
have an evening meal. Bed and Breakfast costs £37 per person and
the evening meal costs £15 per person. How much is the total cost,
if VAT is added at 17½%?

Q8 The owners of a museum are expecting a 14% increase in visitors next year.
This year they had 20 200 visitors.
How many visitors should they expect next year?

Percentages

Q9 Donald earns an annual wage of £23 500. He doesn't pay tax on the first £6400 that he earns. How much income tax does he pay a year if the rate of tax is:
    a) 25%
    b) 40%?

Q10 Tim is choosing between two cars to buy.
The first car is priced at £8495 and has 15% off.
The second car is priced at £8195 and has 12% off.
Which car is the cheapest? Show your working.

Q11 Tanya paid £6500 for her new car. Each year its value decreased by 8%.
    a) How much was it worth when it was one year old?
    b) How much was it worth when it was two years old?

Q12 Jeremy wanted a new sofa for his lounge. A local furniture shop had just what he was looking for — and for only £130.00 + VAT. Jeremy had £150 pounds in his bank account. If VAT was charged at 17½%, could Jeremy afford the sofa?

Here's the 2nd type — finding "something __as a percentage__ of something else" — in this case you're looking at percentage __change__, so don't forget to find the difference in values first.

Q13 During a rainstorm, a water butt increased in weight from 10.4 kg to 13.6 kg. What was the percentage increase (to the nearest percent)?

Q14 An electrical store reduces the price of a particular camera from £90.00 to £78.30. What is the percentage reduction?

Q15 There are approximately 6000 fish and chip shops in the UK. On average, a fish and chip shop gets about 160 visitors each day. Given that the population of the UK is roughly 60 million, approximately what percentage of the population visit a fish and chip shop each day?

Q16 At birth, Veronica was 0.3 m tall. By adulthood she had grown to 1.5 m tall. Calculate her height now as a percentage of her height at birth.

Percentages

Q17   Desmond has a maths exam next week. As part of his revision he attempted 31 questions
on his least favourite topic of percentages. He got 21 questions right on the first attempt.
Two days later he tried all 31 questions again and this time got 29 correct.
   a) What percentage of questions did he get correct on his first attempt?
   b) What percentage of questions did he get correct on his second attempt?
   c) What is the percentage increase in the number of questions Desmond got right?

Q18   I wish to invest £1000 for a period of three years and have decided to place my money
with the Highrise Building Society on 1 January. If I choose to use the Gold Account
I will withdraw the interest at the end of each year. If I choose to use the Silver Account
I will leave the interest to be added to the capital at the end of each year.

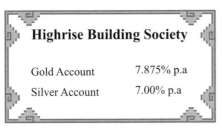

Highrise Building Society

Gold Account   7.875% p.a

Silver Account   7.00% p.a

   a) Calculate the total interest I will receive if I use the
Gold Account.
   b) Calculate the total interest I will receive if I use the
Silver Account.
   After some thought I decide to use the Gold Account
and leave the interest to be added to the capital at the
end of each year.
   c) Calculate the total interest I will now receive from the
Gold Account.

Q19   If $L = MN$, what is the percentage increase in L if M increases by 15% and N increases
by 20%?

Ooh... here's the 3rd type — finding the original value. The bit most people get
wrong is deciding whether the value given represents more or less than 100% of
the original — so always check your answer makes sense.

Q20   In the new year sales Robin bought a tennis racket for £68.00.
The original price had been reduced by 15%. What was the original price?

Q21   There are 360 people living in a certain village. The population of the village has grown
by 20% over the past year.
   a) How many people lived in the village one year ago?
   b) If the village continues to grow at the same rate, how many whole years from today will
it be before the population is more than twice its current size?

Time

Q1 The times below are given using a 24 hour system. Using am or pm, give the equivalent time for a 12 hour clock.

    a) 0500   **c)** 0316   **e)** 2230
    b) 1448   **d)** 1558   **f)** 0001

Q2 The times below are taken from a 12 hour clock. Give the equivalent 24 hour readings.

    a) 11.30 pm   **c)** 12.15 am   **e)** 8.30 am
    b) 10.22 am   **d)** 12.15 pm   **f)** 4.45 pm

Q3 Joe is watching a film. It starts at 19.55 and ends at 22.20.
How many minutes does the film last?

Q4 Find the time elapsed between the following pairs of times:

    a) 0820 on 1 October 2010 and 1620 on the same day
    b) 10.22 pm on 1 October 2010 and 8.22 am the next day
    c) 2.18 am on 1 October 2010 and 2.14 pm later the same day
    d) 0310 on 1 October 2010 and 0258 on 3 October 2010.

Q5 Convert the following into hours and minutes:

    a) 3.25 hours   **b)** 0.4 hours   **c)** 7.3 hours   **d)** 1.2 hours.

Q6 Convert the following into just hours:

    a) 2 hours and 20 minutes
    b) 3 hours and 6 minutes
    c) 20 minutes.

Q7 This timetable refers to three trains that travel from Asham to Derton.
    a) Which train is quickest from Asham to Derton?
    b) Which train is quickest from Cottingham to Derton?

Asham – Derton			
	Train 1	Train 2	Train 3
Asham	0832	1135	1336
Bordhouse	0914	1216	1414
Cottingham	1002	1259	1456
Derton	1101	1404	1602

    c) I live in Bordhouse. It takes me 8 minutes to walk to the train station.
What time must I leave the house by to arrive in Derton before 2.30 pm?

Measures and Conversion Factors

You've got to know all the metric conversion factors — there's no way out of it, you'll just have to sit down and learn them, sorry and all that...

Q1 Express the given quantity in the unit(s) in brackets:

a) 2 m [cm]
b) 3.3 cm [mm]
c) 4 kg [g]
d) 600 g [kg]

e) 650 m [km]
f) 9 kg [g]
g) 7 g [kg]
h) 950 g [kg]

i) 6 m [mm]
j) 2 tonnes [kg]
k) 3000 g [kg]
l) 8 cm 6 mm [mm]

m) 550 kg [tonnes]
n) 3 m 54 cm [cm]
o) 0.7 cm [mm]
p) 4200 ml [l]

Q2 A seamstress needs to cut a 47 cm strip of finest Chinese silk.
a) How many m is this?
b) How many mm is this?

Q3 The priceless Greek statue in my garden is 3 metres tall.
a) How many cm is this?
b) How many mm is this?
c) How many km is this?

Q4 The scale on a map is 1:10 000.
How big are the following in real life? Give your answers in km.
a) a distance of 2 cm on the map
b) a distance of 20 cm on the map
c) a distance of 70 cm on the map
d) an area of 2 cm² on the map?

Maps can be tricky. Best thing is to keep the units the same when you do the initial conversion, then do another conversion to the appropriate units.

Q5 Another map has a scale of 1:3000.
What size on this map are the following?
Give your answers in cm.
a) a distance of 5 km in real life
b) a distance of 1 km in real life
c) an area of 100 m² in real life
d) an area of 50 m² in real life?

Just remember — the distance on the map is unlikely to be larger than the real-life distance.

Q6 Justin is shopping online. He looks up the following exchange rates:

1.60 US Dollars ($) to £1 sterling.

150 Japanese Yen (¥) to £1 sterling.

Calculate to the nearest penny the cost in pounds sterling of each of Justin's purchases:
a) A book costing $7.50
b) An MP3 player costing ¥7660

Scale Drawings

Q1   A rectangular room measures 20 m long and 15 m wide. Work out the measurements for a scale drawing of the room using a scale of 1 cm = 2 m.

Q2   Katie drew a scale drawing of the top of her desk. She used a scale of 1:10. This is her drawing of the computer keyboard. What are the actual dimensions of it?

Q3

| Cupboards | Oven | Cupboards |

This is a scale drawing of part of Paul's kitchen. Measure the width of the gap for the oven.

The drawing uses a scale of 1 : 60.
Work out the maximum width of oven, in cm, that Paul can buy.

Q4   A rectangular room is 4.8 m long and 3.6 m wide.
    a) Make a scale drawing of it using a scale of 1 cm to 120 cm.
    b) On your scale drawing mark a window which has an actual length of 2.4 m on one long wall and mark a door, actual width 90 cm, on one shorter wall.

Q5   The scale on this map is 1 cm : 4 km.

    a) Measure the distance from A to B in cm.

    b) What is the actual distance from A to B in km?

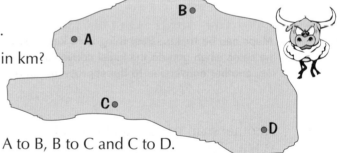

    c) A helicopter flies on a direct route from A to B, B to C and C to D. What is the total distance flown in km?

Q6   Frank has made a scale drawing of his garden to help him plan some improvements. The scale of the drawing is 1 : 70.

    a) Frank wants to put up a fence along the three outside edges of the lawn. How many metres of fencing does he need to buy?

    b) What is the actual area of Frank's patio in m?

Money

To find the best **VALUE FOR MONEY**, start by finding the **AMOUNT PER PENNY** — the more of the stuff you get per penny, the better value it is.

Q1 Which of these boxes of eggs is better value for money?

60p

£1.10

Q2 The small bar of chocolate weighs 50 g and costs 32p.
The large bar weighs 200 g and costs 80p.

a) How many grams do you get for 1p from the small bar?

b) How many grams do you get for 1p from the large bar?

c) Which bar gives you more for your money?

Q3 The large tin of tuna weighs 400 g and costs £1.05.
The small tin weighs 220 g and costs 57p.

a) How many grams do you get for 1p in the large tin?

b) How many grams do you get for 1p in the small tin?

c) Which tin gives better value for money?

Q4 The Bon Voyage Holiday Company are offering an exchange rate of 1.21 Euros for £1 sterling. They are also offering 8.97 Danish kroner for £1 sterling and 1.74 Australian dollars for £1 sterling. Calculate, to the nearest penny, the sterling equivalent of:

a) 220 Euros

b) 686 Danish kroner

c) 1664 Australian dollars

d) 148 Euros

e) 15 Danish kroner

f) 1950 Australian dollars

g) 899 Danish kroner

h) 20 Euros

i) 668 Australian dollars

j) 3389 Danish kroner

k) 1000 Australian dollars

l) 1 Euro

Q5 Neil is going to buy some fabric for a new pair of trousers that he is going to make. A local shop prices the fabric that he would like at £9.84 per square yard. A fabric superstore prices the same fabric at £10.80 per square metre. According to price, where should Neil buy his fabric? (Use the conversion factor 91 cm = 1 yard.)

Interest

You may not have a lot of interest in this page,
but it will be useful to invest some time in it. Ah-ha!

Q1   A financial advisor is asked to calculate the future value of his clients' investments.
Calculate the amount in each of these accounts if:
a) £200 is invested for 10 years at 9% compound interest per annum
b) £500 is invested for 3 years at 7% compound interest per annum
c) £1000 is invested for 12 months at 6.5% compound interest per annum

Q2   Mrs Smith decides to invest £7000 in a savings account. Her bank offers her two
options. In the first option, she can put all her money into an account paying
5% compound interest per annum. In the second option, she can put half of her
investment into an account paying 6% compound interest per annum and the
remaining half into an account paying 4% compound interest per annum.
If she left the investment alone for 3 years,
which is her best option and by how much?

**I'd put my money in
Victorian rolling pins, myself...**

Q3   A man invests in antique elephant sculptures. When he sells his collection he finds that
the increase in value is equivalent to 4% simple interest a year. Calculate how much
each of these sculptures is worth when he sells it:
a) a wooden elephant bought for £420, sold 5 years later
b) a marble elephant bought for £1100, sold 3 years later
c) a plastic elephant bought for £8, sold 25 years later
d) a bronze elephant bought for £81 230, sold 9 years later.

Q4   Julia is opening a bank account. There are three options available — an account that
pays 4% compound interest per year, an account that pays 5% simple interest per year
and an account that pays £5 per month. Which should she choose if she invests:
a) £1000 for 1 year?
b) £3000 for 10 years?
c) £2200 for 25 years?
Show your working for each answer.

Q5   An accountant is looking at some financial records. She needs to work out the principal
amount that was invested a year ago. What was the principal amount invested in:
a) an account containing £278.10 that paid 3% interest?
b) an account containing £837.40 that paid 6% interest?
c) an account containing £1175.20 that paid 4% interest?
d) shares that are worth £8172.24 and have increased in value by 2%?
e) shares that are worth £5049 and have decreased in value by 1%?

Finance Questions

Q1 Alex receives this electricity bill.
Use it to calculate the following:
a) The total amount Alex needs to pay.
b) The service charge as a percentage of the total cost of the bill.
c) The rate of VAT charged on the bill.

Previous meter reading	48 213 kWh
New meter reading	48 697 kWh
Price per kWh	13.1 p
Service charge	£15.40
VAT	£4.73

Q2 Anne buys a tractor on hire purchase.
She pays £17 000 as a deposit and £1800 a month for 5 years.
a) What is the total cost of the tractor?
The deposit was 20% of the cash price of the tractor.
b) What was the cash price of the tractor?
c) What was the extra cost of paying by hire purchase, as a percentage of the cash price?

Q3 Paul earns £34 200 per year. The table shows the tax rates he is charged on his income.
a) How much tax does he pay?
b) What is the average rate of tax that he pays?
Paul receives a bonus of £7300.
c) How much tax will he now pay on his total income?

Amount earned	Tax rate
First £6500	0 %
Next £30 000	20 %
Further income	40 %

Q4 The table on the right shows Hilary's annual budget. It shows her income and essential bills.
a) How much money does she have left after all the bills have been paid?
b) She decides to save 22% of her remaining income. How much money should she put into her savings each month?
c) The gas bill costs 40% more than the average monthly cost in January and 20% less than the average in August.
How much is the gas bill for:
i) January?
ii) August?
d) Hilary shares a house with 2 other people. They split the electricity bill equally. What is the average annual electricity bill for the whole house?
e) Hilary spent £3286.92 on food in a year. How much did she spend per week on average?
f) Hilary buys a car with a cash price of £9500 on hire purchase. She pays a 15% deposit and 30 monthly payments of £280. What is the hire purchase price?

Income	£27 000
Taxes	£6200
Rent	£4800
Electricity	£350
Gas	£300
Water	£120
Transport	£2700
Communication	£530

SECTION TWO — MORE NUMBERS

Rounding Numbers

With all these rounding methods, you need to identify the last digit — e.g. if you're rounding **23.41** to 1 decimal place the last digit is 4. Then look at the next digit to the right. If it's 5 or more you round up, if it's 4 or less you round down.

Q1 Round these numbers to the required number of decimal places:

a) 62.1935 (1 d.p.)   **d)** 19.624328 (5 d.p.)
b) 62.1935 (2 d.p.)   **e)** 6.2999 (3 d.p.)
c) 62.1935 (3 d.p.)   **f)** π (3 d.p.)

Q2 Round these numbers to the required number of significant figures.

a) 1329.62 (3 s.f.)   **d)** 120 (1 s.f.)
b) 1329.62 (4 s.f.)   **e)** 0.024687 (1 s.f.)
c) 1329.62 (5 s.f.)   **f)** 0.024687 (4 s.f.)

Remember — the first significant figure is the first digit which isn't zero.

Q3 $K = 456.9873$
Write K correct to:

a) one decimal place   **d)** three significant figures
b) two decimal places   **e)** two significant figures
c) three decimal places   **f)** one significant figure.

Q4 Calculate the square root of 8. Write your answer to two decimal places.

Q5 Calculate, giving your answers to a sensible degree of accuracy:

a) $\dfrac{42.65 \times 0.9863}{24.6 \times 2.43}$

b) $\dfrac{13.63 + 7.22}{13.63 - 7.22}$

Rounding Numbers

Whenever a measurement is rounded off to a given unit, the <u>actual measurement</u> can be anything up to <u>half a unit bigger or smaller</u>.

1) <u>90 m</u> to the <u>nearest 10 metres</u> could be anything from <u>85 m to 95 m</u>. (But not <u>exactly</u> equal to 95 m, or it would be rounded up to 100 m).

2) <u>700 people</u> to the nearest <u>10 people</u> could be anything between <u>695 people and 704 people</u>. (Because this only involves <u>whole</u> numbers.)

Q6 A bumper bag of icing sugar weighs 23.4 kg. What is this correct to the nearest kilogram?

Q7 David divides £15.20 by 3. What is the answer to the nearest penny?

Q8 The great racing driver Speedy Wheelman covered 234.65 miles during the course of one of his races. Give this distance correct to the nearest mile.

Q9 Jack's company pays his travel expenses.
They round the distance he drives to the nearest mile, and then pay 20p for every mile. In one week, Jack drives 95.45 miles. How much money can Jack claim back?

Q10 A pack of three model cars costs £14.30. John wants to work out what one model car would cost. What is the answer correct to the nearest penny?

Q11 Pru measured the length of her bedroom as 2.345 metres.
Give this measurement in cm, correct to the nearest centimetre.

Q12 At a golf club, a putting green is given as being 5 m long to the nearest metre. Give the range of values that the actual length of the green could be.

Q13 Carlo weighs himself on some scales that are accurate to the nearest 10 g. The digital display shows his weight as 142.46 kg.
 a) What is the maximum that he could weigh?
 b) What is the minimum that he could weigh?

You need to add the errors for all the sides together.

Q14 a) The length of a rectangle is measured as 12 ± 0.1 cm. The width of the same rectangle is measured as 4 ± 0.1 cm. Calculate the perimeter of the rectangle, and give the maximum possible error.
 b) A rectangle measures $A ± x$ cm in length and $B ± y$ cm in width. The formula $P = 2(A + B)$ is used to calculate the perimeter, P, of the rectangle. What is the maximum possible error in P?

Accuracy and Estimating

We're back to significant figures again. Still, it's all good practice, and practice makes...

1) For fairly CASUAL MEASUREMENTS, 2 SIGNIFICANT FIGURES are most appropriate.

Cooking — 250 g (2 s.f.) of sugar, not 253 g (3 s.f) or 300 g (1 s.f.).

2) For IMPORTANT OR TECHNICAL THINGS, 3 SIGNIFICANT FIGURES are essential.

A length that will be cut to fit — you'd measure a shelf as 25.6 cm long, not 26 cm or 25.63 cm.

3) Only for REALLY SCIENTIFIC WORK would you need over 3 SIGNIFICANT FIGURES.

Only someone really keen would want to know the length of a piece of
string to the nearest tenth of a millimetre — like 34.46 cm, for example.

Q1 A field is roughly rectangular with a length of 33 m 48 cm and a width of
24 m 13 cm. Farmer Jim needs to calculate the area of the field so that he
knows how much fertiliser to buy. Calculate the area of the field in m² to:
  a) 2 d.p.
  b) 3 s.f.
  c) State which of parts **a)** and **b)** would be the more reasonable value to use.

Just think casual, technical or really scientific...

Q2 Decide on an appropriate degree of accuracy for the following:
  a) the total dry weight, 80872 kg, of the space shuttle OV-102
  Columbia with its 3 main engines
  b) the distance of 3.872 miles from Mel's house to Bryan's house
  c) 1.563 m of fabric required to make a bedroom curtain
  d) 152.016 kg of coal delivered to Jeff's house
  e) 6 buses owned by the Partridge Flight Bus Company
  f) the maximum night temperature of 11.721 °C forecast for
  Birmingham by a TV weather presenter.

Q3 Round each of the following to an appropriate degree of accuracy:
  a) 42.798 g of sugar used to make a cake
  b) a hall carpet of length 7.216 m
  c) 3.429 g of $C_6H_{12}O_6$ (sugar) for a scientific experiment
  d) 1.132 litres of lemonade used in a fruit punch
  e) 0.541 miles from Jeremy's house to the nearest shop
  f) 28.362 miles per gallon.

Accuracy and Estimating

Q4   Without using your calculator find approximate answers to the following:

a) 6560 × 1.97

b) 8091 × 1.456

c) 38.45 × 1.4237 × 5.0002

d) 45.34 ÷ 9.345

e) 34504 ÷ 7133

f) $\dfrac{55.33 \times 19.345}{9.23}$

g) 7139 × 2.13

h) 98 × 2.54 × 2.033

i) 21 × 21 × 21

j) 8143 ÷ 81

k) 62000 ÷ 950

l) π ÷ 3

Turn these into nice easy numbers that you can deal with without a calculator.

Q5   At the start of the week, a shop had approximately 15 000 cartons of broccoli juice in stock. The shop sold 1483 cartons on Monday, 2649 on Tuesday, 1539 on Wednesday, 1478 on Thursday and 2958 on Friday. Estimate the number of cartons remaining.

Q6   Estimate the area under the graph.

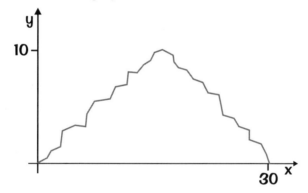

Q7   A supermarket chain sold 14634 tins of beans during a four week period.

a) If the supermarkets were open every day of the week, how many days did it take to sell the 14634 tins of beans?

b) What was the average number of tins of beans sold each day?

c) Show your working for a rough estimate to **b)** to check that your answer is of the right order of magnitude.

"of the right order of magnitude" is just a posh way to say "the right size", by the way.

Q8   π is the number of times that the diameter of a circle divides into the circumference. Many values have been used as estimates of π — here are a few examples:

$$3, \ \frac{22}{7}, \ \sqrt{10}, \ \frac{255}{81}, \ 3\frac{17}{120}.$$

a) Use your calculator to give each estimate correct to 7 decimal places.

b) Which is the most accurate estimate for π?

Q9   Showing all your working, estimate the value of the following:

a) $\dfrac{144.5 + 49.1}{153.2 - 41.2}$

b) $\dfrac{18.2 \times 10.7}{\sqrt{398.6}}$

c) $\dfrac{2021.23 \times 4.0436}{20.33 \times 4.902}$

d) $\dfrac{(9.2)^2 \div 10.3}{4.306 \times 5.011}$

Accuracy and Estimating

Q10 Estimate the areas of the following:

a)

44.3 cm

26.4 cm

b)

3.89 km

5.2 km

Q11 Joan needs to estimate the size of her bedroom so that she can buy enough paint to cover the walls. Two of the walls measure 2.86 m by 3.16 m, and the other two walls measure 2.86 m by 3.42 m.
  a) Estimate the area that Joan needs to paint in m².
  b) If one tin of paint will cover 15 m², how many tins of paint will Joan need to paint her bedroom?

Q12 Estimate these volumes:

a)

10 cm

22.3 cm

b)

4 cm

9.7 cm

3.1 cm

Q13 Mark wants to buy some tropical fish. The pet shop owner tells him that he will need a tank with a volume of at least 7000 cm³. Estimate whether Mark's tank will be big enough.

10.4 cm

14.8 cm

29.6 cm

Q14 Here is a sequence of square numbers. Use it to estimate (to 1 dp) the square roots below.

12	13	14	15	16	17	18	19	20
144	169	196	225	256	289	324	361	400

  a) $\sqrt{405}$ **b)** $\sqrt{270}$ **c)** $\sqrt{250}$ **d)** $\sqrt{375}$ **e)** $\sqrt{391}$

Q15 Estimate the following square roots, to 1 dp:

  a) $\sqrt{48}$ **c)** $\sqrt{84}$ **e)** $\sqrt{98}$

  b) $\sqrt{118}$ **d)** $\sqrt{17}$ **f)** $\sqrt{34}$

> Start with square roots that you know — and use them to make an educated guess.

Q16 Now estimate these — again, to 1 dp:

  a) $\sqrt{41}$ **c)** $\sqrt{30}$ **e)** $\sqrt{180}$

  b) $\sqrt{200}$ **d)** $\sqrt{150}$ **f)** $\sqrt{140}$

Upper and Lower Bounds

Q1 Jodie weighs herself on some scales that are accurate to the nearest 10 grams. The digital display shows her weight as 64.78 kg.
a) What is the maximum that she could weigh?
b) What is the minimum that she could weigh?

Q2 Katherine is going on holiday and weighs her luggage to check that it isn't over the weight allowance. She knows that her scales weigh to the nearest 100 g. The scales read that her bag weighs 13.8 kg. What is the most that Katherine's bag could weigh?

Q3 Sandra has a parcel to post. To find out how much it will cost she weighs it.
a) A set of kitchen scales, that weigh to the nearest 10 g, shows that the parcel weighs 90 g. Write down the largest weight that the parcel could be.
b) Next she weighs the parcel on a different set of kitchen scales, which are accurate to the nearest 5 g. The parcel weighs 95 g. Write down the upper and lower bounds of the weight of the package according to these scales.
c) The post office weighs the parcel to the nearest gram on some electronic scales. It weighs 98 g. Can all the scales be right?

Q4 A rectangular rug is 1.8 metres long and 0.7 metres wide. Both measurements are given correct to one decimal place.
a) State the minimum possible length of the rug.
b) Calculate the maximum possible area of the rug, to 2 d.p.

Q5 $R = \dfrac{S}{T}$ is a formula used by stockbrokers.

$S = 940$, correct to 2 significant figures and $T = 5.56$, correct to 3 significant figures.
a) For the value of S, write down the upper bound and the lower bound.
b) For the value of T, write down the upper bound and the lower bound.
c) Calculate the upper bound and lower bound for R.
d) Write down the value of R correct to an appropriate number of significant figures.

Remember — you don't always get the maximum value by using the biggest input values.

Upper and Lower Bounds

Q6 $A = 13$, correct to 2 significant figures.
        $B = 12.5$, correct to 3 significant figures.
   a) For the value of A, write down the upper bound and the lower bound.
   b) For the value of B, write down the upper bound and the lower bound.
   c) Calculate the upper bound and lower bound for C when $C = AB$.

Q7   Ash wants to put a new carpet in his living room. He has measured the
        floor as being 3.4 m × 5.2 m to the nearest 10 cm. What area of carpet
        should Ash buy to make sure he has enough to cover the whole floor?

Q8   Vince ran a 100 m race in 10.3 seconds. If the time was measured to the nearest
        0.1 seconds and the distance to the nearest metre, what is the maximum possible
        value of his average speed, in metres per second?

Q9   A lorry travelled 125 kilometres in 1 hour and 50 minutes. If the time was measured
        to the nearest 10 minutes and the distance to the nearest five kilometres, what was the
        maximum value of the average speed of the lorry, in kilometres per hour?

Q10   Jimmy, Sarah and Douglas are comparing their best times for
        running the 1500 m.
        Jimmy's best time is 5 minutes 30 seconds measured to the
        nearest 10 seconds.
        Sarah's best time is also 5 minutes 30 seconds, but measured to
        the nearest 5 seconds.
        Douglas' best time is 5 minutes 26 seconds measured to the
        nearest second.

   a) What are the upper and lower bounds for Sarah's best time?
   b) Of the three Douglas thinks that he is the quickest at running the 1500 m.
        Explain why this may not be the case.

Conversion Graphs and Gradients

Q1 This graph can be used to convert the distance (kilometres) travelled in a taxi to the fare payable (£). How much will the fare be if you travel:

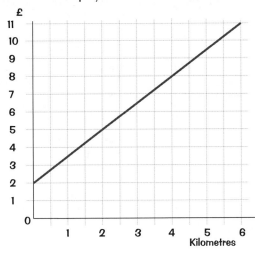

a) 2 kilometres?

b) 5 kilometres?

c) 10 kilometres?

d) Mike lives 4.5 kilometres away from his friend. Is £16 enough money for Mike to get a taxi to his friend's house and back?

Q2 a) 80 km is roughly equal to 50 miles. Use this information to draw a conversion graph Use the graph to estimate the number of miles equal to:

i) 20 km
ii) 70 km
iii) 90 km

When you've got to draw your own conversion graph, your best bet is to work out a few different values, and mark them on the graph first.

b) How many km are equal to:

i) 40 miles?
ii) 10 miles?
iii) 30 miles?

Q3 Describe the meaning of the gradient in each of the graphs below:

a)

b)

c)

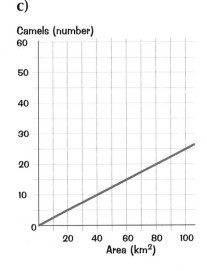

D/T and S/T Graphs

You need to remember what the different bits of a travel graph mean — what it looks like when **stopped**, **changing speed** and **coming back** to the starting point.

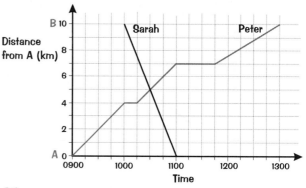

Q1 Peter set out from A at 0900 to walk to B.
- **a)** How far did he walk in the 1st hour?
- **b)** He stopped twice; how long was each stop?
- **c)** What was his speed after the second stop?

At 1000 Sarah set out on her bike to ride from B to A.
- **d)** What time did she arrive at A?
- **e)** What was her average speed?
- **f)** At what time did Peter and Sarah pass each other?

Q2 Dave drives a bus from Kendal to Ingleton and back again. The bus company graphed the journey to help them organise their bus schedules.

- **a)** How long did it take to get to Ingleton?
- **b)** How much time was spent driving to and from Ingleton excluding stops?
- **c)** What was the average speed for the journey from Kendal to Ingleton?
- **d)** What was Dave's fastest speed?
- **e)** The transport manager wants Dave to reduce the duration of the stops on the Kendal to Ingleton route so that he can make another journey from Kendal to Windermere starting at 1630. Would this be possible?

Q3 Mr. Smith leaves home at 0730 to go to work. He walks at a steady 6 km/h for 2 km. He catches the 0755 train which takes 35 mins to travel 50 km. He then walks 3 km to work and arrives at 0900.

Draw a graph to show this.
How long did he wait at the station for the train?

D/T and S/T Graphs

Q4 A train operator plans to purchase a new engine. They've graphed the journeys made by five engines over a 100 km stretch of track to help them decide which one is best.

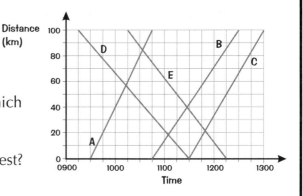

a) Calculate the speed of each train and state which one was the fastest.

b) How could you tell by looking at the diagram which was the fastest and which was the slowest?

Q5 On sports day the first three in the 1000 m race ran as shown in the graph below.

a) Which runner, A, B or C, won the race?

b) How long did the winner take?

c) Which runner kept up a steady speed?

d) What was that speed
  i) in m/min?
  ii) km/h?

e) Which runner achieved the fastest speed and what was that speed?

Q6 Two cars start a journey at midday (1200) — one travels from town A to village B, and the other from village B to town A. A and B are 80 km apart. The car from town A travels at an average speed of 48 km/h and the other car, from village B, at 60 km/h.

a) Draw a graph to show these journeys.

b) At what time do the cars pass? (approx.)

c) How far from A are they when they pass?

> Use the speeds given to work out the time it takes for each car to travel the 80 km.

Q7 A girl set off on a walk. She started at 0915 and walked at a steady speed for 9 km before stopping at 1100 for a 20 min break. She then set off again at a steady speed and walked 8 km, stopping at 1300 for 45 mins. After lunch she walked at 3½ km/h for 2½ hrs to reach her destination.

a) Draw a graph to show this walk.

b) How far did she walk altogether?

c) What was the average speed for the whole walk?

d) What was her fastest walking speed?

D/T and S/T Graphs

Q8 This is a speed-time graph of a train journey.

a) What was the maximum speed?
b) How long did the train travel at a constant speed for in total?
c) What was the rate of deceleration?

Q9 Andrew's cycle computer plots a graph of his journey but only shows his speed.

He wants to know how far he travelled.
a) Calculate the distance travelled in:
  i) The first two hours.
  ii) The last two hours.
b) Calculate the total distance travelled.

 Add up all the little trapeziums to find the whole area — easy trapeasy...

Q10 This graph shows the speed of a train during a period of six seconds.

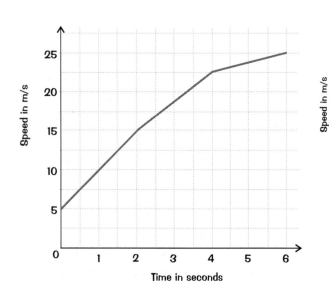

Estimate the total distance travelled in the period of six seconds by dividing the area into three trapeziums of equal width.

Q11 This graph shows the speed of a train during a period of eight seconds.

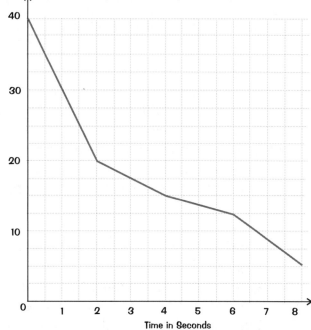

Estimate the total distance travelled in the period of eight seconds by dividing the area into four trapeziums of equal width.

Coordinates

Q1 ABCD is a <u>parallelogram</u>. A is (-1, 3), B is (-2,-1) and C is (4,-1).
Draw axes with *x* from -3 to 5 and *y* from -2 to 4.
Plot A, B and C then find the <u>missing coordinates</u> for D.

Q2 Draw axes with *x* from -9 to 9 and *y* from -12 to 12.
On the <u>same</u> set of axes draw the following shapes and find their
<u>missing pair of coordinates</u>.

a) ABCD is a <u>square</u>
A is (1, 1)
B is ?
C is (-3,-3)
D is (-3, 1)

c) ABCD is a <u>rectangle</u>
A is ?
B is (3,-8)
C is (3,-6)
D is (-5,-6)

e) ABCD is a <u>parallelogram</u>
A is (-2,-10)
B is (4,-10)
C is (6,-12)
D is ?

b) ABCD is a <u>parallelogram</u>
A is (2, 8)
B is (6, 8)
C is ?
D is (1, 5)

d) ABCD is a <u>kite</u>
A is (-9, 3)
B is (-6, 8)
C is (-4, 8)
D is ?

f) ABCD is a <u>parallelogram</u>
A is (-8, 10)
B is (-6, 10)
C is ?
D is (-5, 12)

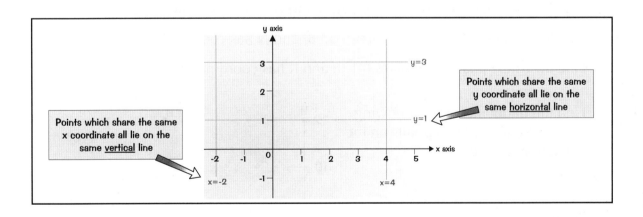

Q3 ABCD is a <u>rectangle</u> with the line *x* = 0
as a <u>line of symmetry</u>.
Draw axes with *x* from -3 to 3 and
y from -3 to 3.
If A = (-2,-2) and B is (-2, 1), find the
<u>coordinates of C and D</u>.

I'm afraid you'll just have to get the hang of using things like "the line x = 4", as they seem to prefer it to "a vertical line through the point 4 on the horizontal axis". Yeah, that is a bit long winded, I guess — so maybe they've got a point...

44

Midpoints of Line Segments

Q1 Find the midpoint of the line segment AB, where A and B have coordinates:

a) A(2,3) B(4,5)

b) A(1,8) B(10,2)

c) A(0,11) B(11,11)

d) A(3,15) B(14,3)

e) A(6,7) B(0,0)

f) A(16,16) B(3,3)

g) A(8,33) B(32,50)

h) A(17,28) B(44,13)

ahh... nice'n'easy...

Your answers should be coordinates too.

Q2 Anna is designing the plan of a kitchen using some computer aided design software. The coordinates of the corners of the room on screen are (0, 10), (220, 10), (0, 260), (220, 260). She needs to enter the coordinates of the ceiling light, which will be exactly in the centre of the room. What will the coordinates of the light be?

Q3 Find the midpoints of each of these line segments :

a) Line PQ, where P has coordinates (–1,5) and Q has coordinates (5,6).

b) Line AB, where A has coordinates (–3,3) and B has coordinates (4,0).

c) Line RS, where R has coordinates (4,–5) and S has coordinates (0,0).

d) Line EF, where E has coordinates (–1,–3) and F has coordinates (3,1).

e) Line GH, where G has coordinates (10,13) and H has coordinates (–6,–7).

f) Line CD, where C has coordinates (–4,6) and D has coordinates (12,–7).

g) Line MN, where M has coordinates (–5,–8) and N has coordinates (–21,–17).

h) Line JK, where J has coordinates (–1,0) and K has coordinates (–9,–14).

Q4 Find the midpoints of the following line segments between points on the diagram to the right:

a) Line segment AB

b) Line segment CG

c) Line segment EL

d) Line segment DK

e) Line segment EF

f) Line segment HC

g) Line segment BL

h) Line segment DJ

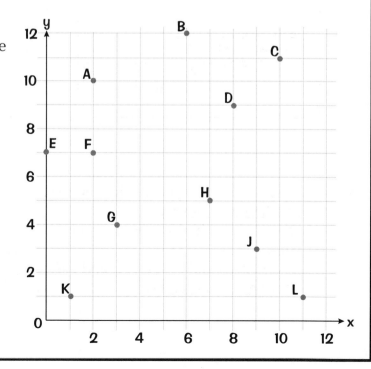

SECTION THREE — GRAPHS

Lengths of Line Segments

Q1 Find the length of each of the line segments on this graph.

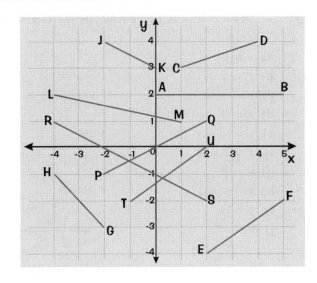

Q2 The coordinates of four points are A(2,1), B(6,4), C(7,0) and D(3,−3). Calculate the distances:

a) AB   **b)** BC   **c)** CD   **d)** BD   **e)** AC

f) What shape is ABCD?

Q3 Find the length of line MN, where M and N have coordinates:

a) M(6,3) N(2,8)   **d)** M(9,5) N(4,8)

b) M(1,5) N(8,12)   **e)** M(10,4) N(10,0)

c) M(0,1) N(7,3)   **f)** M(12,6) N(13,0)

Q4 Find the length of line PQ, where P and Q have coordinates:

a) P(2,−3) Q(3,0)   **d)** P(−6,−1) Q(7,−9)

b) P(1,−8) Q(4,3)   **e)** P(12,−3) Q(−5,5)

c) P(0,−1) Q(2,−3)   **f)** P(−10,−2) Q(−2,−8)

OK, so there's a few negative numbers creeping in here, but just do them in the same way.

Q5 Line segment AB has a length of 5 units. The coordinates of A are (−1, 2) and the coordinates of B are (2, x). What are the two possible values of x?

Straight Line Graphs

Q1   Which letters represent the following lines:

a) $x = y$
b) $x = 5$
c) $y = -x$
d) $x = 0$
e) $y = -7$
f) $x + y = 0$
g) $y = 5$
h) $x - y = 0$
i) $y = 0$
j) $x = -7$

Don't get confused if you've got "x + y = ... " — just rearrange the equation to "y = -x + ..." and as if by magic, you've got a line you recognise.

Q2   Complete the following table for the line $y = 3x - 1$:

x	-4	-3	-2	-1	0	1	2	3	4
3x									
y = 3x−1									

Plot these points on graph paper and hence draw the graph of $y = 3x - 1$.
Use a scale of 1 cm for 2 units on the y-axis and 2 cm for 1 unit on the x-axis.

Q3   Complete the following table for the line $y = \frac{1}{2}x - 3$:

x	-6	-4	-2	0	2	4	6
½ x							
y=½x-3							

Plot these points on graph paper and hence draw the graph of $y = \frac{1}{2}x - 3$.

Straight Line Graphs

If you know it's a straight line, you only really need <u>two</u> points, but it's always a <u>good idea</u> to plot three — it's a bit of a safety net, really.

Q4 Complete this table of values for $y = 2x + 3$:

X	0	3	8
y			

Plot these points on graph paper and draw the graph of $y = 2x + 3$.
Use your graph to find:

a) The value of y when $x = 5$
b) The value of y when $x = 2$
c) The value of x when $y = 11$
d) The value of x when $y = 17$

Q5 Complete this table of values for $y = \frac{1}{4}x - 3$:

X	-8	-4	8
y			

Plot these points on graph paper and draw the graph of $y = \frac{1}{4}x - 3$.
Use your graph to find:

a) The value of y when $x = 2$
b) The value of y when $x = 0$
c) The value of x when $y = -2$
d) The value of x when $y = -1.5$

Q6 The cost of electricity is calculated using the formula:
Total cost = Fixed charge + (cost per unit × number of units).
Customers can choose two different methods of payment:
Method A: Fixed charge £10, cost per unit 25p
Method B: Fixed charge £40, cost per unit 5p
Copy and complete this table:

Number of Units used	0	100	200	300
Cost using method A				
Cost using method B				

Plot these points on a graph (put the number of units on the horizontal axis, and the cost on the vertical axis):

a) Use your graph to find the total cost when 70 units are used for:
  i) Method A
  ii) Method B

b) Miss Wright used 75 units. Which method should she use to minimize her bill, Method A or Method B?

c) Use your graph to work out how many units Miss Wright would have to use for both methods to cost the same amount.

y = mx + c

Writing the equation of a line in the form y = mx + c gives you a nifty way of finding the gradient and y-intercept. Remember that — it'll save you loads of time. Anything for an easy life...

Q1 For each of the following lines, give the gradient and the coordinates of the point where the line cuts the *y*-axis.

a) $y = 4x + 3$

b) $y = 3x - 2$

c) $y = 2x + 1$

d) $y = -3x + 3$

e) $y = 5x$

f) $y = -2x + 3$

g) $y = -6x - 4$

h) $y = x$

i) $y = -\frac{1}{2}x + 3$

j) $y = \frac{1}{4}x + 2$

k) $3y = 4x + 6$

l) $2y = -5x - 4$

m) $8y = 4x - 12$

n) $3y = 7x + 5$

o) $x + y = 0$

p) $x - y = 0$

q) $y - x = 3$

r) $x - 3 = y$

s) $y - 7 = 3x$

t) $y - 5x = 3$

u) $y + 2x + 3 = 0$

v) $y - 2x - 4 = 0$

I know these are a bit algebra-ish, but don't worry, they won't bite.

Q2 What is the gradient of:

a) line A

b) line B

c) line C

d) line D

e) line E

f) line F

g) line G

h) line H

i) line I

j) line J

k) a line parallel to A

l) a line parallel to B

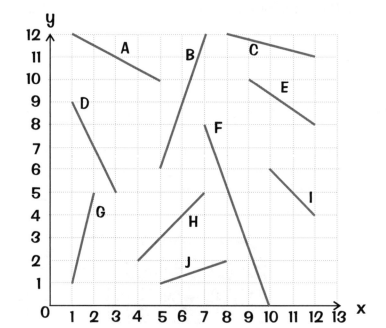

Uphill gradients are always positive, downhill always negative. Impressed?
Hmmm....thought not. Can be a bit of an uphill battle, these.

Q3 Find the equation of the straight line which passes through:

a) (3, 7) and has a gradient of 1

b) (2, 8) and has a gradient of 3

c) (–3, 3) and has a gradient of 2

d) (4, –4) and has a gradient of –1

e) (–1, 7) and has a gradient of –3

f) (4, –11) and has a gradient of –2.

y = mx + c

Q4 Find the equations of the following lines:

a) A
b) B
c) C
d) D
e) E
f) F

Yeah, OK, this sounds a bit scary, but just work out the gradient (m) and look at the y-intercept (c) and pop them back into "y = mx + c"... easy lemons.

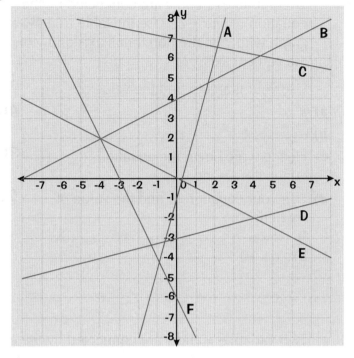

Q5 What is the value of x or y if:

a) the point $(x, 13)$ is on the line $y = 3x + 1$
b) the point $(x, -2)$ is on the line $y = \frac{1}{2}x - 6$
c) the point $(4, y)$ is on the line $y = 2x - 1$
d) the point $(-3, y)$ is on the line $y = -3x$?

Q6 Which of the following points lie on the line $y = 3x - 1$?
$(7, 20)$, $(6, 15)$, $(5, 14)$

Q7 What is the gradient of the lines joining the points:

a) $(3, 5)$ and $(5, 9)$
b) $(6, 3)$ and $(10, 5)$
c) $(-6, 4)$ and $(-3, 1)$
d) $(8, 2)$ and $(4, 10)$
e) $(8, 5)$ and $(6, 4)$
f) $(-3, -1)$ and $(1, -4)$?

Q8 Lauren works in a ski resort grading ski runs. A blue run has a gradient less-steep than -0.2, a red is steeper, but has a gradient shallower than -0.25. Anything steeper is a black. A run is 1.75 km long and descends 400 metres. What colour should Lauren grade it?

Q9 Write down the equation of the line which passes through the points:

a) $(2, 2)$ and $(5, 5)$
b) $(1, 3)$ and $(4, 12)$
c) $(-2, -3)$ and $(5, 11)$
d) $(1, 0)$ and $(5, -12)$
e) $(-5, 6)$ and $(-1, -2)$
f) $(4, 23)$ and $(-2, -7)$.

Here's a bit more practice with those gradients. Thought you'd like that.

Equations from Graphs

Q1 Two variables x and y are connected by the equation $y = mx + c$. Use the table to draw a graph with x on the horizontal axis and y on the vertical axis.

x	1	3	5	8
y	9	17	25	37

Use your graph to find the value of:

a) m

b) c

c) Hence write down the equation connecting x and y.

d) Use your equation to find the value of y when:

　　i)　$x = 6$

　　ii)　$x = 10$

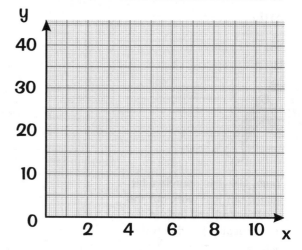

Q2 Two variables x and y are connected by the equation $y = ax + b$.

Here are some values of x and y.

x	4	9	16	25
y	5	7.5	11	15.5

Use the table to draw a graph. Plot x on the horizontal axis using a scale of 1 cm to 2 units and y on the vertical using a scale of 1 cm to 1 unit.

Use your graph to find:

a) the value of a

b) the value of b.

c) Write down the equation connecting x and y.

Q3 CGPtronics semiconductor company plans to release a new microprocessor. It costs a certain amount to design, and a certain amount per unit to manufacture. The table below shows the total production cost for producing different numbers of microprocessors.

Units	10 000	30 000	50 000	70 000
Production cost	£23 000	£29 000	£35 000	£41 000

a) Plot the data from the table on a graph.

b) Use the graph to work out the cost of designing the microprocessor.
Use this to work out the manufacturing cost per unit.

c) Write down an equation connecting the number of units made to the production cost.

d) CGPtronics want to sell the microprocessors for 80p each.
On the same set of axes, plot a graph showing the revenue from selling different numbers of microprocessors.

　　revenue = value of sales

e) How many microprocessors will CGPtronics have to sell to break even?

Equations from Graphs

Q4   The table shows the labour costs of having a television repaired. The cost consists of a fixed rate call-out charge plus a charge for each ten minutes that the repair man works.

Time (min)	10	20	30	40	50
Cost (£)	8	10		14	16

Plot the points on a graph with the time on the horizontal axis and the cost on the vertical axis.

a) Find a formula connecting the cost (C) in pounds and the time (M) in minutes.

b) What is the fixed rate call-out charge?

c) Use your graph to find the cost for 30 minutes.

d) Use your formula to find the cost for:
    i)   80 minutes
    ii)   100 minutes
    iii)   3 hours.

Q5   Dominic works in the finance office of a small company. He has been asked to review the company's energy costs, and is writing a report comparing two energy providers. The table below shows their prices, which vary with the amount of energy used.

Number of units used	100	200	300	500
Provider A price (£)	8	11	14	20
Provider B price (£)	5	10	15	25

Plot the points for both providers on the same graph with the number of units used on the horizontal axis and the price (£) on the vertical axis.

a) Find the formula connecting price (P) and number of units (N) used for each energy provider.

b) Use your formulas to calculate the price each energy provider would charge for:
    i)   400 units
    ii)   700 units.

c) Use the graph to determine the number of units the company would need to use for there to be no difference in price between the two providers.

Graphs to Recognise

Q1   Identify the type of graph shown below.
Choose from straight line, quadratic, cubic and reciprocal:

a)

b)

c)

d)

e)

f)

g)

h)

i)

j)

You'll need to be able to <u>sketch a graph</u> from <u>memory</u> — yeah, scary huh.
Remember — the <u>5 main ones</u> are <u>straight line</u> (easy), <u>x^2</u> (buckets), <u>x^3</u> (wiggly),
<u>$1/x$</u> (2 bits and "x=0" missing) and <u>k^x</u> (almost flat on the left, steep on the right).

Graphs to Recognise

Q2   Here are some equations, and there are some curves below.
Match the equations to the curves.

a) $y = -2x - 1$ **d)** $y = -x^2 + 3$ **g)** $y = -\frac{1}{2}x^3 + 2$ **j)** $y = \frac{2}{x}$

b) $y = 3x$ **e)** $y = x^2$ **h)** $y = x^3$ **k)** $y = \frac{1}{x^2}$

c) $y = x^2 + 2$ **f)** $y = 2x^3 - 3$ **i)** $y = -\frac{3}{x}$ **l)** $y = -\frac{1}{x^2}$

i)

ii)

iii)

iv)

v)

vi)

vii)

viii)

ix)

x)

xi)

xii)

Quadratic Graphs

So, you can spot a quadratic graph at ten paces, but can you draw one...

The simplest quadratic graph is $y = x^2$

x	-4	-3	-2	-1	0	1	2	3	4
y	16	9	4	1	0	1	4	9	16

$$y = ax^2 + bx + c$$

There will always be an x^2 term. The value of 'a' cannot be zero

Sometimes either 'b' or 'c' could be zero. Even if both were equal to zero, the graph would still be quadratic

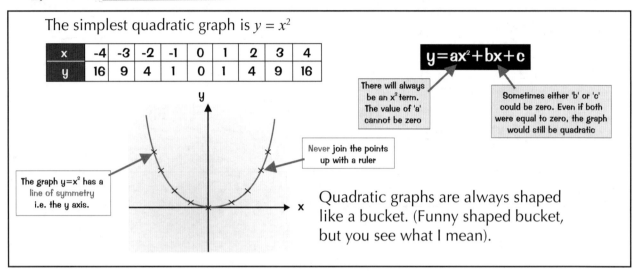

Never join the points up with a ruler

The graph $y = x^2$ has a line of symmetry i.e. the y axis.

Quadratic graphs are always shaped like a bucket. (Funny shaped bucket, but you see what I mean).

Q1 Complete this <u>table of values</u> for the quadratic graph $y = 2x^2$.

a) Draw axes with x from -4 to 4 and y from 0 to 32.
b) Plot these 9 points and join them with a <u>smooth curve</u>.
c) Label your graph.

x	-4	-3	-2	-1	0	1	2	3	4
$y = 2x^2$	32	18					8		

Remember to square first then $\times$ 2

Q2 Complete this table of values for the graph $y = x^2 + x$.

x	-4	-3	-2	-1	0	1	2	3	4
x^2	16	9					4		
$y = x^2 + x$	12					2			

By putting more steps in your table of values, the arithmetic is easier

a) Draw axes with x from -4 to 4 and y from 0 to 20.
b) Plot the points and join them with a smooth curve.
c) Draw and label the <u>line of symmetry</u> for the quadratic graph $y = x^2 + x$.

If the x^2 term has a <u>minus</u> sign in front of it, the bucket will be turned <u>upside down</u>.

Q3 a) Complete this table of values for the graph $y = 3 - x^2$.
b) Draw the graph $y = 3 - x^2$ for x from -4 to 4.
c) State the <u>maximum value</u> of the graph $y = 3 - x^2$.

x	-4	-3	-2	-1	0	1	2	3	4
$-x^2$	-16						-4		
$y = 3 - x^2$	-13						-1		

Cubic Graphs

You go about a cubic in the same way as you would a quadratic — but you should get a different-shaped graph, of course. It's always a good idea to put <u>lots of steps</u> in the <u>table of values</u> — that way it's <u>easier to check</u> any points that look wrong.

Q1 Complete this table of values for $y = x^3$:

x	-3	-2	-1	0	1	2	3
y=x³							

Draw the graph of $y = x^3$.

Q2 Complete this table of values for $y = -x^3$:

x	-3	-2	-1	0	1	2	3
y=-x³							

Draw the graph of $y = -x^3$.

Q3 Complete this table of values for $y = x^3 + 4$:

x	-3	-2	-1	0	1	2	3
x³							
y=x³+4							

Draw the graph of $y = x^3 + 4$.

Remember — no rulers.

Q4 Complete this table of values for $y = -x^3 - 4$:

x	-3	-2	-1	0	1	2	3
-x³							
y=-x³-4							

Draw the graph of $y = -x^3 - 4$.

Q5 Look at your graphs for questions 1 and 3.
What has been done to graph 1 to change it into graph 3?
Without plotting a table of values draw the graph of $y = x^3 - 4$.

Q6 Look at your graphs for questions 2 and 4.
What has been done to graph 2 to change it into graph 4?
Without plotting a table of values draw the graph of $y = -x^3 + 4$.

Graphs of Other Equations

Here are some equations and shapes that are even more alien... Just go about doing them the same way as a cubic or quadratic and you'll be fine. Don't skip stages when you're working through it — errors will then become much harder to spot.

The two halves of a 1/x graph never touch and are symmetrical around y = x and y = -x.

Q1 Complete this table of values for $y = 1/x$.

a) Draw axes with x from -4 to 4 and y from -1 to 1.

b) Plot these points and join them with a smooth curve.

c) Label your graph.

x	-4	-3	-2	-1	0	1	2	3	4
y = 1/x		-0.33			n/a				0.25

The 0's just there to fool you — any equation with A/x in it makes a graph that never passes through x = 0.

A/x^2 graphs are similar to 1/x graphs but the two halves are next to each other.

Q2 Complete this table of values for $y = 3/x^2$.

x	-4	-3	-2	-1	0	1	2	3	4
$1/x^2$			0.25			1		0.11	
$y=3/x^2$						3			

A can be any number — positive or negative

a) Draw axes with x from -4 to 4 and y from 0 to 3.

b) Plot the points and join them with a smooth curve.

c) Draw and label the line of symmetry for the quadratic graph $y = 3/x^2$.

k^x graphs are always above the x-axis and pass through the point (0, 1).

Q3 a) Complete this table of values for $y = 2^x$.

b) Draw the graph $y = 2^x$ for x from -4 to 4.

c) Why do k^x graphs always pass through (0, 1)?

k can be any positive number

x	-4	-3	-2	-1	0	1	2	3	4
$y=2^x$				0.5	1		4		

All these types of equations can be combined — see what shape of graph you get.

Q4 a) Complete this table of values for $y = 3^x - 6/x$.

b) Draw the graph $y = 3^x - 6/x$ for x from -3 to 3.

x	-3	-2	-1	0	1	2	3
3^x			0.33		3		
$6/x$						3	
$y=3^x - 6/x$					-3		

Powers and Roots

Hang on there. Before you try this page, make sure you know all the rules for dealing with powers...

The small number is called the **power** or **index number**. Remember the plural of index is **indices**.

$5^4 = 5 \times 5 \times 5 \times 5 =$ _____
we say "five to the power four"

$8^3 = 8 \times 8 \times 8 =$ _____
we say "eight to the power three" or "eight cubed"

To save time try using the power button on your calculator

Q1 Complete the following:
a) $2^4 = 2 \times 2 \times 2 \times 2 \quad =$
b) $10^3 = 10 \times 10 \times 10 \quad =$
c) $3^5 = 3 \times \ldots \quad =$
d) $4^6 = 4 \times \ldots \quad =$
e) $1^9 = 1 \times \ldots \quad =$
f) $5^6 = 5 \times \ldots \quad =$

Q2 Simplify the following:
a) $2 \times 2 \times 2 \times 2 \times 2 \times 2 \times 2 \times 2$
b) $12 \times 12 \times 12 \times 12 \times 12$
c) $x \times x \times x \times x \times x \times x$
d) $m \times m \times m$
e) $y \times y \times y \times y$
f) $z \times z \times z \times z \times z \times z$

Q3 Complete the following (the first one has been done for you):
a) $10^2 \times 10^3 = (10 \times 10) \times (10 \times 10 \times 10) = 10^5$
b) $10^3 \times 10^4 = \qquad =$
c) $10^4 \times 10^2 = \qquad =$
d) $10^5 \times 10^3 = \qquad =$
e) What is the <u>quick method</u> for writing down the final result in **b)**, **c)** and **d)**?

Easy — you'll have learnt this from your power rules.

Q4 Complete the following (the first one has been done for you):
a) $2^4 \div 2^2 = \dfrac{(2 \times 2 \times 2 \times 2)}{(2 \times 2)} = 2^2$
b) $2^5 \div 2^2 = \dfrac{(2 \times 2 \times 2 \times 2 \times 2)}{(2 \times 2)} =$
c) $4^5 \div 4^3 = \dfrac{(4 \times 4 \times 4 \times 4 \times 4)}{} =$
d) $8^5 \div 8^2 = \qquad =$

e) What is the quick method for writing down the final result in **b)**, **c)** and **d)**?

Q5 Which of the following are <u>true</u>?
a) $2^4 \times 2^6 = 2^{10}$
b) $2^2 \times 2^3 \times 2^4 = 2^9$
c) $2^3 \times 2^2 = 2^6$
d) $4^{10} \times 4^4 \times 4^2 = 4^{18}$
e) $2^1 \times 2^3 \times 2^4 = 2^8$
f) $10^4 \times 10^2 = 10^8$
g) $2^{20} \div 2^5 = 2^4$
h) $3^{12} \div 3^4 = 3^8$
i) $4^6 \div 6^4 = 4^2$
j) $10^{20} \div 10^3 = 10^{17}$
k) $4^6 \div (4^2 \times 4^3) = 4^1$
l) $9^2 \times (9^{30} \div 9^{25}) = 9^{10}$

Q6 Remove the brackets from the following and express as a single power:
a) $(3^4 \times 3^2) \div (3^6 \times 3^3)$
b) $(4^{10} \times 4^{12}) \times 4^3$
c) $10^2 \div (10^3 \times 10^{12})$
d) $(3^6)^{-2}$
e) $4^2 \times 4^{-1} \times 4^6 \times (4^2 \div 4^3)$
f) $(5^2 \times 5^3) \div (5^6 \div 5^4)$

Powers and Roots

Simplify the expressions in questions 7 to 11. Give your answers to 3 s.f. where necessary.

Q7 a) $(6.5)^3$

b) $(0.35)^2$

c) $(15.2)^4$

d) $(0.04)^3$

e) $\sqrt{5.6}$

f) $\sqrt[3]{12.4}$

g) $\sqrt{109}$

h) $\sqrt[3]{0.6}$

i) $(1\frac{1}{2})^2$

j) $\sqrt{4\frac{3}{4}}$

k) $\left(\frac{5}{8}\right)^3$

l) $\sqrt[3]{\frac{9}{10}}$

Q8 a) $(2.4)^2 + 3$

b) $5.9 - (1.2)^3$

c) $\sqrt[3]{5.6} + (4.2)^2$

d) $(6.05)^3 - \sqrt[3]{8.4}$

e) $6.1[35.4 - (4.2)^2]$

f) $95 - 3(\sqrt[3]{48} - 2.6)$

g) $1\frac{1}{2}[4 + (2\frac{1}{4})^2]$

h) $19 - 4[(\frac{1}{4})^2 + ((\frac{5}{8})^3)]$

i) $15\frac{3}{5} - 2\frac{1}{2}\left[(1\frac{3}{4})^3 - \sqrt[3]{1\frac{1}{2}}\right]$

Q9 a) 5^{-3}

b) 2^{-2}

c) 16^{-4}

d) $(1.5)^{-1}$

e) $5^{\frac{1}{2}}$

f) $6^{\frac{1}{3}}$

g) $9^{\frac{1}{5}}$

h) $(4.2)^{\frac{2}{3}}$

i) $(1\frac{1}{4})^{-3}$

j) $(2\frac{3}{5})^{\frac{1}{5}}$

k) $(5\frac{1}{3})^{-2}$

l) $(10\frac{5}{6})^{\frac{5}{6}}$

Remember — fractional powers mean roots.

Q10 a) $\sqrt{(1.4)^2 + (0.5)^2}$

b) $5.9[(2.3)^{\frac{1}{4}} + (4.7)^{\frac{1}{2}}]$

c) $2.5 - 0.6[(7.1)^{-3} - (9.5)^{-4}]$

d) $(8.2)^{-2} + (1.6)^4 - (3.7)^{-3}$

e) $\dfrac{3\sqrt{8} - 2}{6}$

f) $\dfrac{15 + 3\sqrt{4.1}}{2.4}$

g) $3\sqrt{4.7} - 4\sqrt{2.1}$

h) $\dfrac{(2\frac{1}{4})^{-2} - (3\frac{1}{2})^{\frac{1}{2}}}{4.4}$

Q11 a) $(2\frac{1}{4})^3 - (1.5)^2$

b) $(3.7)^{-2} + (4\frac{1}{5})^{\frac{1}{4}}$

c) $\sqrt[3]{5\frac{1}{3}} \times (4.3)^{-1}$

d) $(7.4)^{\frac{1}{3}} \times (6\frac{1}{4})^3$

e) $\dfrac{\sqrt{22\frac{1}{2}} + (3.4)^2}{(6.9)^3 \times 3.4}$

f) $\dfrac{(15\frac{3}{5})^2 \times (2.5)^{-3}}{3 \times 4\frac{1}{4}}$

g) $5[(4.3)^2 - (2.5)^{\frac{1}{2}}]$

h) $\dfrac{3.5(2\frac{1}{6} - \sqrt{4.1})}{(3.5)^2 \times (3\frac{1}{2})^{-2}}$

i) $\dfrac{1\frac{1}{2} + \frac{1}{4}[(2\frac{2}{3})^2 - (1.4)^2]}{(3.9)^{-3}}$

j) $\sqrt[3]{2.73} + 5\sqrt{2}$

Sequences

Q1 For each of the sequences below, write down the next three numbers and the rule that you used.

a) 1, 3, 5, 7,...

b) 2, 4, 8, 16,...

c) 3, 30, 300, 3000,...

d) 3, 7, 11, 15,...

e) 19, 14, 9, 4, –1,...

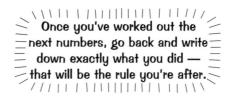

Once you've worked out the next numbers, go back and write down exactly what you did — that will be the rule you're after.

Q2 For the following, use the rule given to generate the first 5 terms of the sequence.

a) $3n + 1$, when $n = 1, 2, 3, 4$ and 5.

b) $5n – 2$, when $n = 1, 2, 3, 4$ and 5.

c) n^2, when $n = 1, 2, 3, 4$, and 5.

d) $n^2 – 3$, when $n = 1, 2, 3, 4$, and 5.

Q3 Write down an expression for the nth term of the following sequences:

a) 2, 4, 6, 8, …

b) 1, 3, 5, 7, …

c) 5, 10, 15, 20, …

d) 5, 8, 11, 14, …

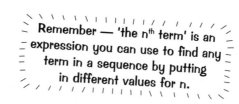

Remember — 'the nth term' is an expression you can use to find any term in a sequence by putting in different values for n.

Q4 In the following sequences, write down the next 3 terms and the nth term:

a) 7, 10, 13, 16,...

b) 12, 17, 22, 27,...

c) 6, 16, 26, 36,...

d) 54, 61, 68, 75,...

Sequences

Q5 The first five terms of a sequence are: 10, 20, 15, 17½, 16¼...
a) Write down the next 4 terms.
b) Explain how you would work out the 10th term.

Q6

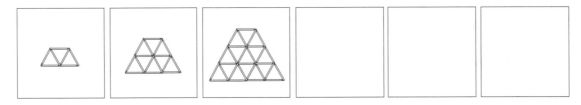

The pattern above is based on individual triangles.
a) Write down the number of individual triangles in each group shown above.
b) Work out the number of individual triangles that would be in each of the next three groups.
c) Find a formula for the number of individual triangles in the *n*th term of the pattern.

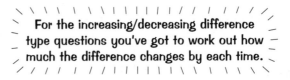

For the increasing/decreasing difference type questions you've got to work out how much the difference changes by each time.

Q7 Write down the next three terms and *n*th term of:

a) 5, 8, 12, 17,...
b) 6, 9, 14, 21,...
c) 9, 12, 19, 30,...
d) 14, 19, 27, 38,...

e) 729, 243, 81, 27,...
f) 31250, 6250, 1250, 250,...
g) 12288, 3072, 768, 192,...
h) 5103, 1701, 567, 189,...

Q8 Hannah is tiling her kitchen floor. She's making a square pattern with grey and white tiles. In the centre there will be a grey tile. The rest of the pattern will be made up of alternating grey and white tiles, with the four corner tiles of the square being grey.
Assume that *n* = 1 in the pattern shown opposite.

Work out, in terms of *n*, the formula for:
a) the number of grey tiles Hannah will need to buy
b) the number of white tiles she will need to buy
c) the total number of tiles needed.

Basic Algebra

Q1 Work out the following temperature changes:
   a) 20 °C to -7 °C
   b) -10 °C to -32 °C
   c) -17 °C to -5 °C
   d) -3 °C to 15 °C
   e) -31 °C to -16 °C
   f) -5 °C to -17 °C

Q2 Which is larger and by how much?
   a) $-12 + 7 - 4 + 6 - 2 + 7$ or **b)** $-30 + 26 - 3 - 7 + 17$

Q3 Simplify: **a)** $4x - 5x + 3x - x + 2x - 7x$ **b)** $30y - 10y + 2y - 3y + 4y - 5y$

Q4 Find the value of xy and $\dfrac{x}{y}$ for each of the following:
   a) $x = -100$ $y = 10$
   b) $x = 24$ $y = -4$
   c) $x = -48$ $y = -3$
   d) $x = 0$ $y = -4$

Q5 Find the value of $(a - b) \div (c + d)$ when $a = 10$, $b = -26$, $c = -5$ and $d = -4$.

Q6 Simplify the following:
   a) $2x \times -3y$
   b) $-8a \times 2b$
   c) $-4x \times -2x$
   d) $4p \times -4p$
   e) $-30x \div -3y$
   f) $50x \div -5y$
   g) $10x \div -2y$
   h) $-30x \div -10x$
   i) $40ab \div -10ab$
   j) $70x^2 \div -7x^2$
   k) $-36x^2 \div -9x$
   l) $40y^2 \div -5y$

Q7 Simplify the following by collecting like terms together:
   a) $3x^2 + 4x + 12x^2 - 5x$
   b) $14x^2 - 10x - x^2 + 5x$
   c) $12 - 4x^2 + 10x - 3x^2 + 2x$
   d) $20abc + 12ab + 10bac + 4b$
   e) $8pq + 7p + q + 10qp - q + p$
   f) $15ab - 10a + b - 7a + 2ba$
   g) $4pq - 14p - 8q + p - q + 8p$
   h) $13x^2 + 4x^2 - 5y^2 + y^2 - x^2$
   i) $11ab + 2cd - ba - 13dc + abc$
   j) $3x^2 + 4xy + 2y^2 - z^2 + 2xy - y^2 - 5x^2$

Basic Algebra

Remember **FOIL** for multiplying brackets... don't want to miss any terms now, do you...

First   Outside   Inside   Last

$(F + x)(F - x)$ then $(O + x)(x - O)$ then $(x + I)(I - x)$ then $(x + L)(x - L)$

Q8 Multiply out the brackets and simplify where possible:

a) $4(x + y - z)$

b) $x(x + 5)$

c) $-3(x - 2)$

d) $7(a + b) + 2(a + b)$

e) $3(a + 2b) - 2(2a + b)$

f) $4(x - 2) - 2(x - 1)$

g) $4e(e + 2f) + 2f(e - f)$

h) $14(2m - n) + 2(3n - 6m)$

i) $4x(x + 2) - 2x(3 - x)$

j) $3(2 + ab) + 5(1 - ab)$

k) $(x - 2y)z - 2x(x + z)$

l) $4(x - 2y) - (5 + x - 2y)$

m) $a - 4(a + b)$

n) $4pq(2 + r) + 5qr(2p + 7)$

o) $x^2(x + 1)$

p) $4x^2\left(x + 2 + \dfrac{1}{x}\right)$

q) $8ab(a + 3 + b)$

r) $7pq\left(p + q - \dfrac{1}{p}\right)$

s) $4[(x + y) - 3(y - x)]$

Q9 For each of the large rectangles below, write down the area of each of the small rectangles and hence find an expression for the area of each large rectangle.

a)

b)

c)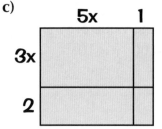

Q10 A rectangular bar of chocolate consists of 20 small rectangular pieces. The size of a small rectangular piece of chocolate is 2 cm by x cm.

a) Write down an expression for the perimeter of the whole bar.

b) Write down an expression for the area of the whole bar.

c) If I ate 6 small rectangular pieces of chocolate, what is the area of the remaining bar?

Q11 All the expressions below have a^2 as a common factor. Factorise each of them.

a) $a^2b + a^2c$

b) $5a^2 + 13a^2b$

c) $2a^2b + 3a^2c$

d) $a^3 + a^2y$

e) $2a^2x + 3a^2y + 4a^2z$

f) $a^2b^2 + a^3c^2$

Q12 Factorise and simplify the following:

a) $4xy^2z + 8xyz^2$ b) $8x^2yz^2 + 12xy^2z$ c) $8xyz + 16x^2yz$ d) $20x^2y^2z^2 + 16xyz^2$

Basic Algebra

Q13 Multiply out the brackets and simplify your answers where possible:
- **a)** $(x - 3)(x + 1)$
- **b)** $(x - 3)(x + 5)$
- **c)** $(x + 10)(x + 3)$
- **d)** $(x - 5)(x - 2)$
- **e)** $(x + 2)(x - 7)$
- **f)** $(4 - x)(7 - x)$
- **g)** $(2 + 3x)(3x - 1)$
- **h)** $(3x + 2)(2x - 4)$
- **i)** $(x - 3)(4x + 1)$
- **j)** $2(2x + y)(x - 2y)$
- **k)** $4(x + 2y)(3x - 2y)$
- **l)** $(3x + 2y)^2$

Q14 A rectangular pond has length $(3x - 2)$ m and width $(5 - x)$ m.
Write down a simplified expression for:
- **a)** the pond's perimeter
- **b)** the pond's area.

Q15 Using the fact that $a^2 - b^2 = (a + b)(a - b)$, factorise the following expressions:
- **a)** $x^2 - 9$
- **b)** $y^2 - 16$
- **c)** $25 - z^2$
- **d)** $36 - a^2$
- **e)** $4x^2 - 9$
- **f)** $1 - 9x^2y^2$
- **g)** $25 - 16z^2$
- **h)** $144 - y^4$
- **i)** $x^4 - 36$
- **j)** $x^4 - y^4$
- **k)** $49x^4y^4 - 1$
- **l)** $100x^2 - 144y^2$

Q16 Find the product of $5x - 2$ and $3x + 2$.

Q17 Find the square of $2x - 1$.

Q18 Find simplified expressions for the perimeter *and* the area of the following shapes.

a)

b)

c)

d)

Q19 Factorise the following expressions:
- **a)** $x + xy + 3y + 3$
- **b)** $4y + 2xy + 5x + 10$

Eeeek — loads
of questions...

Algebraic Fractions

Q1 Simplify the following by cancelling down where possible:

a) $\dfrac{27x^4y^2z}{9x^3yz^2}$

b) $\dfrac{48a^2b^2}{(2a)^2c}$

c) $\dfrac{3xyz}{9x^2y^3z^4}$

d) $\dfrac{4p^3q^3}{(2pr)^3}$

e) $\dfrac{42d^3}{2(7d^2)}$

f) $\dfrac{16(fh)^2}{4(gh)^3}$

g) $\dfrac{78j^2k}{13jkl^3}$

h) $\dfrac{111m^3n^3}{(11mn)^3}$

Q2 Multiply out the following. Simplify your answers as much as possible.

a) $\dfrac{x^2}{y} \times \dfrac{2}{x^3}$

b) $\dfrac{3a^4}{2} \times \dfrac{b}{a^2}$

c) $\dfrac{2x}{y^2} \times \dfrac{y^3}{4x^3}$

d) $\dfrac{3pq}{2} \times \dfrac{4r^2}{9p}$

e) $\dfrac{10z^3}{xy} \times \dfrac{4x^3}{5z}$

f) $\dfrac{30a^2b^2c^2}{7} \times \dfrac{21c^2}{ab^3}$

g) $\dfrac{4}{x} \times \dfrac{x^3}{2} \times \dfrac{x}{10}$

h) $\dfrac{2a^2}{3} \times \dfrac{9b}{a} \times \dfrac{2a^2b}{5}$

i) $\dfrac{5a^2b}{b} \times \dfrac{3a^2c^3}{10bd}$

j) $\dfrac{p^2}{pq^2} \times \dfrac{q^2}{p}$

k) $\dfrac{90r^2}{14t} \times \dfrac{7t^3}{30r}$

l) $\dfrac{400d^4}{51e^5} \times \dfrac{102d^2e^4}{800e^2f}$

It helps if you can cancel some factors before multiplying.

Q3 Divide the following. Simplify your answers as much as possible.

a) $\dfrac{4x^3}{y} \div \dfrac{2x}{y^2}$

b) $\dfrac{ab}{c} \div \dfrac{b}{c}$

c) $\dfrac{30x^3}{y^2} \div \dfrac{10x}{y}$

d) $\dfrac{pq}{r} \div \dfrac{2}{r}$

e) $\dfrac{e^2f^2}{5} \div \dfrac{ef}{10}$

f) $\dfrac{5x^3}{y} \div \dfrac{1}{y}$

g) $\dfrac{16xyz}{3} \div \dfrac{4x^2}{9}$

h) $\dfrac{20a^3}{b^3} \div \dfrac{5}{b^2}$

i) $\dfrac{25a^3}{b^3} \div \dfrac{5}{b^2}$

j) $\dfrac{4x}{y^4z^4} \div \dfrac{2}{y^2z^3}$

k) $\dfrac{3m}{2n^2} \div \dfrac{m}{4n}$

l) $\dfrac{70f^3}{g} \div \dfrac{10f^4}{g^2}$

Q4 Solve the following equations for x:

a) $\dfrac{20x^4y^2z^3}{7xy^5} \times \dfrac{14y^3}{40x^2z^3} = 5$

b) $\dfrac{48x^5y^2}{12z^3} \div \dfrac{16x^2y^2}{z^3} = 2$

Algebraic Fractions

OK, I guess it gets a bit tricky here — you've got to cross-multiply to get a common denominator before you can get anywhere with adding or subtracting.

Q5 Add the following. Simplify your answers as much as possible.

a) $\dfrac{3}{2x} + \dfrac{y}{2x}$

b) $\dfrac{1}{x} + \dfrac{y}{x}$

c) $\dfrac{4xy}{3z} + \dfrac{2xy}{3z}$

d) $\dfrac{(4x+2)}{3} + \dfrac{(2x-1)}{3}$

e) $\dfrac{5x+2}{x} + \dfrac{2x+4}{x}$

f) $\dfrac{6x}{3} + \dfrac{2x+y}{6}$

g) $\dfrac{x}{8} + \dfrac{2+y}{24}$

h) $\dfrac{x}{10} + \dfrac{y-1}{5}$

i) $\dfrac{2x}{3} + \dfrac{2x}{4}$

j) $\dfrac{x}{6} + \dfrac{5x}{7}$

k) $\dfrac{x}{3} + \dfrac{x}{y}$

l) $\dfrac{zx}{4} + \dfrac{x+z}{y}$

Q6 Subtract the following. Simplify your answers as much as possible.

a) $\dfrac{4x}{3} - \dfrac{5y}{3}$

b) $\dfrac{4x+3}{y} - \dfrac{4}{y}$

c) $\dfrac{(8x+3y)}{2x} - \dfrac{(4x+2)}{2x}$

d) $\dfrac{(9-5x)}{3x} - \dfrac{(3+x)}{3x}$

e) $\dfrac{10+x^2}{4x} - \dfrac{x^2+11}{4x}$

f) $\dfrac{2x}{3} - \dfrac{y}{6}$

g) $\dfrac{z}{5} - \dfrac{2z}{15}$

h) $\dfrac{4m}{n} - \dfrac{m}{3}$

i) $\dfrac{2b}{a} - \dfrac{b}{7}$

j) $\dfrac{(p+q)}{2} - \dfrac{3p}{5}$

k) $\dfrac{p-2q}{4} - \dfrac{2p+q}{2}$

l) $\dfrac{3x}{y} - \dfrac{4-x}{3}$

Q7 Simplify the following:

a) $\left(\dfrac{a}{b} \div \dfrac{c}{d}\right) \times \dfrac{ac}{bd}$

b) $\dfrac{x^2+xy}{x} \times \dfrac{z}{xz+yz}$

c) $\dfrac{(p+q)}{r} \times \dfrac{3}{2(p+q)}$

d) $\dfrac{m^2n}{p} + \dfrac{mn}{p^2}$

e) $\dfrac{1}{x+y} + \dfrac{1}{x-y}$

f) $\dfrac{2}{x} - \dfrac{3}{2x} + \dfrac{4}{3x}$

g) $\dfrac{a+b}{a-b} + \dfrac{a-b}{a+b}$

h) $\dfrac{1}{4pq} \div \dfrac{1}{3pq}$

i) $\dfrac{x}{8} - \dfrac{x+y}{4} + \dfrac{x-y}{2}$

66

Formulas from Words

It's no big mystery — algebra is just like normal sums, but with the odd letter or two stuck in for good measure.

Q1 Write an algebraic expression for each of these:

a) To find *y* add 5 to *x*
b) To find *y* multiply *x* by 7 and add 4
c) To find *y* subtract 7 from *x* and divide by 3

d) To find *y* square 6 and add it to *x*
e) Square *x* then divide by 8 to find *y*
f) *y* equals to the square of *x*, divided by 12

Q2 Tickets for a football match cost £25 each.
a) Write a formula to calculate the cost, *c*, of *n* tickets.
b) A booking fee of £1.25 is added to each ticket bought online. Write a formula to calculate the cost of *n* tickets bought online.

Q3 There are *n* books in a pile. Write an expression for the number of books in:
a) A pile with 23 more books
b) A pile with 14 fewer books
c) A pile with twice as many books

d) *x* piles each with *n* books in them
e) A warehouse filled with a square of book piles *x* piles long each side.

Q4 a) This square has sides of length *d* cm.

  i) What is its perimeter?

  ii) What is its area?

b) For the triangle below write expressions for:

  i) Its perimeter

  ii) Its area.

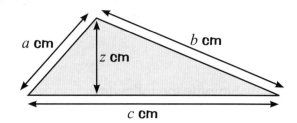

Q5 The cost (*C*) of hiring a mountain bike is £10, plus £5 for each hour you use the bike (*h*). Write down a formula that can be used for working out the cost of hiring a bike.

Q6 The cost per person of a flight from Manchester to Aberdeen is £73 plus £27 tax and an extra £15 for each piece of luggage. Write down a formula to calculate the total cost (*T*) of a flight for *p* people with a total of *l* pieces of luggage.

Q7 The number of sheep (*S*) that a dragon can eat per day is 3 plus a third of its wingspan in metres (*w*). Write an expression to calculate how many sheep a dragon can eat in *d* days.

Section Four — Algebra

Solving Equations

Q1 When 1 is added to a number and the answer then trebled, it gives the same result as doubling the number and then adding 4. Find the number.

Q2 Solve the following:
- **a)** $3x + 1 = 2x + 6$
- **b)** $4x + 3 = 3x + 7$
- **c)** $5x - 1 = 3x + 19$
- **d)** $x + 2 = \frac{1}{2}x - 1$
- **e)** $x + 15 = 4x$
- **f)** $3x + 3 = 2x + 12$

Q3 Solve the following:
- **a)** $3x - 8 = 7$
- **b)** $2(x - 3) = -2$
- **c)** $4(2x - 1) = 60$
- **d)** $2x - 9 = 25$
- **e)** $\frac{24}{x} + 2 = 6$
- **f)** $5x - 2 = 6x - 7$
- **g)** $30 - \frac{x}{2} = 28$

Q4 A square has sides of length $(x + 1)$ cm. Find the value of x if:
- **a)** the perimeter of the square is 66 cm
- **b)** the perimeter of the square is 152.8 cm.

With these wordy ones, you just have to write your own equation from the information you're given.

Q5 Mr Smith sent his car to the local garage. He spent £x on new parts, four times this amount on labour and finally £29 for a safety test. If the total bill was for £106.50, find the value of x.

Q6 Joan, Kate and Linda win £2400 between them. Joan gets a share of £x, whilst Kate gets twice as much as Joan. Linda's share is £232 less than Joan's amount.
- **a)** Write down an expression for the amounts Joan, Kate and Linda win.
- **b)** Write down an equation in terms of x, and solve it.
- **c)** Write down the amounts Kate and Linda receive.

It's easy — you just put the 2 bits together and there's your equation. Then all you've got to do is solve it...

Q7 For what value of x is the expression $14 - \frac{x}{2}$ equal to the value of $\frac{3x - 4}{2}$?

Q8 Two men are decorating a room. One has painted 20 m² and the other only 6 m². They continue painting and manage to paint another x m² each. If the first man has now painted exactly three times the area painted by the second man, find the value of x.

Q9 Carol's father was 24 years old when Carol was born. Now he is four times as old as Carol. How old is Carol?

Q10 Mr Jones is 4 years older than his wife and 31 years older than his son. Their three ages add up to 82 years. If Mr Jones is x years old, find the value of x and find the ages of his wife and son.

Solving Equations

Q11 Solve:

a) $2(x - 3) - (x - 2) = 5$

b) $5(x + 2) - 3(x - 5) = 29$

c) $2(x + 2) + 3(x + 4) = 31$

d) $10(x + 3) - 4(x - 2) = 7(x + 5)$

e) $5(4x + 3) = 4(7x - 5) + 3(9 - 2x)$

f) $3(7 + 2x) + 2(1 - x) = 19$

g) $\frac{x}{3} + 7 = 12$

h) $\frac{x}{10} + 18 = 29$

i) $17 - \frac{x^2}{3} = 5$

j) $41 - \frac{x}{11} = 35$

k) $\frac{x}{100} - 3 = 4$

l) $\frac{120}{x} = 16$

Q12 All the angles in the diagram on the right are right angles.

a) Write down an expression for the perimeter of the shape.

b) Write down an expression for the area of the shape.

c) For what value of x will the perimeter be half the numerical value of the area?

Q13 Solve the following:

a) $2x^2 = 18$

b) $2x^2 = 72$

c) $3x^2 = 27$

d) $4x^2 = 36$

e) $5x^2 = 5$

f) $12x^2 = 108$

Q14 Solve the following:

a) $5(x - 1) + 3(x - 4) = -11$

b) $3(x + 2) + 2(x - 4) = x - 3(x + 3)$

c) $\frac{3x}{2} + 3 = x$

d) $3(4x + 2) = 2(2x - 1)$

e) $\frac{5x + 7}{9} = 3$

f) $\frac{2x + 7}{11} = 3$

Q15 Solve the following:

a) $\frac{y}{2} + 2 = 13$

b) $\frac{3x}{4} - 2 = 4$

c) $\frac{2z}{5} - 3 = -5$

d) $\frac{1}{5}(x - 4) = 3$

e) $\frac{2}{3}(x + 1) = 16$

f) $\frac{3}{5}(4x - 3) = 15$

g) $\frac{8}{x^2} = \frac{32}{36}$

h) $\frac{12}{5x^2} = \frac{3}{20}$

i) $\frac{14}{3x^2} = \frac{2}{21}$

Q16 A train travels at 70 mph for x hours and then at 80 mph for $3\frac{3}{4}$ hours. If the train covers 405 miles of track, find the value of x.

Q17 Solve the following:

a) $\frac{4x + 3}{2} + x = \frac{5x + 41}{4}$

Remember to do the same to the top and the bottom.

b) $\frac{5}{7}(x - 2) - \frac{3}{4}(x + 3) = -4$

Q18 A triangle has lengths as shown on the right. Find the length of each side, if the length of AC exceeds that of AB by ½ cm.

Rearranging Formulas

Rearranging is getting the letter you want out of the formula and making it the subject. And it's exactly the same method as for solving equations, which can't be bad.

Q1 Rearrange the following formulas to make the letter in brackets the new subject.

a) $g = 10 - 4h$ (h)

b) $d = \frac{1}{2}(c + 4)$ (c)

c) $j = -2(3 - k)$ (k)

d) $a = \frac{2b}{3}$ (b)

e) $f = \frac{3g}{8}$ (g)

f) $y = \frac{x}{2} - 3$ (x)

g) $s = \frac{t}{6} + 10$ (t)

h) $p = 4q^2$ (q)

Q2 Jason is saving up to go travelling next year and has got a temporary job selling cars. He is paid a basic wage of £500 a month, plus a bonus of £50 for each car he sells. He has a spreadsheet to keep track of his money, which calculates his wages (£*w*) after working for *m* months and selling *c* cars, using the following formula:
$$w = 500m + 50c$$
a) Rearrange the formula to make *c* the subject.
b) Find the number of cars Jason needs to sell in 11 months to earn £12 100.

Q3 The cost of hiring a car is £28 per day plus 25p per kilometre.
a) Find the cost of hiring the car for a day and travelling:
    i) 40 km
    ii) 80 km

b) Write down a formula to give the cost of hiring a car (£*c*) for one day, and travelling *n* km.
c) Rearrange the formula to make *n* the subject.
d) How many kilometres can you travel, during one day, if you have a budget of:
    i) £34,   **ii)** £50,   **iii)** £56.50.

Q4 A website offering digital photo printing charges 12p per print plus 60p postage.
a) Find the cost of ordering:
    i) 12 prints.
    ii) 24 prints.
b) Write down a formula for the cost C, in pence, of ordering *x* prints.
c) Rearrange the formula to make *x* the subject.
d) A regular customer is looking through old receipts to check she has been charged the right amount. How many prints should she have received in each of her last three transactions if she was charged:
    i) £4.92
    ii) £6.36
    iii) £12.12.

Rearranging Formulas

Q5 Mrs Smith buys x jumpers for £J each and sells them in her shop for a total price of £T.

    a) Write down an expression for the amount of money she paid for all the jumpers.

    b) Using your answer to **a)**, write down a formula for the profit £P Mrs Smith makes selling all the jumpers.

    c) Rearrange the formula to make J the subject.

    d) Given that Mrs Smith makes a profit of £156 by selling 13 jumpers for a total of £364 find the price she paid for each jumper originally.

Q6 Rearrange the following formulas to make the letter in brackets the new subject.

    a) $y = x^2 - 2$ (x) **d)** $f = \dfrac{10 + g}{3}$ (g) **g)** $v^2 = u^2 + 2as$ (a)

    b) $y = \sqrt{(x + 3)}$ (x) **e)** $w = \dfrac{5 - z}{2}$ (z) **h)** $v^2 = u^2 + 2as$ (u)

    c) $r = \left(\dfrac{s}{2}\right)^2$ (s) **f)** $v = \dfrac{1}{3}x^2 h$ (x) **i)** $t = 2\pi\sqrt{\dfrac{l}{g}}$ (g)

Q7 Rearrange the following formulas, by collecting terms in x and looking for common factors, to make x the new subject.

    a) $xy = z - 2x$ **e)** $xy = xz - 2$

    b) $ax = 3x + b$ **f)** $2(x - y) = z(x + 3)$

    c) $4x - y = xz$ **g)** $xyz = x - y - wz$

    d) $xy = 3z - 5x + y$ **h)** $3y(x + z) = y(2z - x)$

Q8 Rearrange the following to make the letter in brackets the new subject.

    a) $pq = 3p + 4r - 2q$ (p) **g)** $\sqrt{hk^2 - 14} = k$ (k)

    b) $fg + 2e = 5 - 2g$ (g) **h)** $2\sqrt{x} + y = z\sqrt{x} + 4$ (x)

    c) $a(b - 2) = c(b + 3)$ (b) **i)** $\dfrac{a}{b} = \dfrac{1}{3}(b - a)$ (a)

    d) $pq^2 = rq^2 + 4$ (q) **j)** $\dfrac{m + n}{m - n} = \dfrac{3}{4}$ (m)

    e) $4(a - b) + c(a - 2) = ad$ (a) **k)** $\sqrt{\dfrac{(d - e)}{e}} = 7$ (e)

    f) $\dfrac{x^2}{3} - y = x^2$ (x) **l)** $\dfrac{x - 2y}{xy} = 3$ (y)

These are getting quite tricky — you've got to <u>collect like terms</u>, before you can make anything else the subject.

Q9 Rearrange the following formulas to make y the new subject.

    a) $x(y - 1) = y$ **c)** $x = \dfrac{y^2 + 1}{2y^2 - 1}$

    b) $x(y + 2) = y - 3$ **d)** $x = \dfrac{2y^2 + 1}{3y^2 - 2}$

Simultaneous Equations

To solve simultaneous equations from scratch, you've got to get rid of either x or y first — to leave you with an equation with just one unknown in it.

Q1 Solve the following simultaneous equations:

a) $4x + 6y = 16$
$x + 2y = 5$

b) $3x + 8y = 24$
$x + y = 3$

c) $3y - 8x = 24$
$3y + 2x = 9$

d) $3y - 10x - 17 = 0$
$\frac{1}{3}y + 2x - 5 = 0$

e) $\frac{x}{2} - 2y = 5$
$12y + x - 2 = 0$

f) $x + y = \frac{1}{2}(y - x)$
$x + y = 2$

Q2 Two farmers are buying livestock at a market. Farmer Ed buys 6 sheep and 5 pigs for £430 and Farmer Jacob buys 4 sheep and 10 pigs for £500.

a) If sheep cost £x and pigs cost £y, write down the two purchases as a pair of simultaneous equations.

b) Solve for x and y.

Q3 Solve the following simultaneous equations:

a) $y = x$
$y = 9 - 2x$

b) $y = 2x + 1$
$2y = 8 + x$

c) $y = 4 - 2x$
$x + y = 3$

d) $y = 3 - x$
$3x + y = 5$

e) $2x + y = 6$
$y = 3x + 1$

f) $y = 2x$
$y = x + 1$

g) $x + y = 5$
$2x - 1 = y$

h) $2y = 3x$
$y = x + 1$

i) $y = x - 3$
$y + x = 7$

Q4 Isobel is buying sweets. She weighs out 20 jellies and 30 toffees which come to 230 g. She takes one of each off the scales, and the weight drops to 221 g. How much does an individual toffee weigh?

Q5 Find the value of x and y for each of the following rectangles, by first writing down a pair of simultaneous equations and then solving them.

a) [rectangle: top $3y + 2x$, left $3x + y$, right 6, bottom 18]

b) [rectangle: top 12, left $4y + 5x$, right 7, bottom $2x - 3y$]

c) [rectangle: top $4x - 6y$, left $y + x$, right 2, bottom 13]

Q6 Two customers enter a shop to buy milk and cornflakes. Mrs Smith buys 5 cartons of milk and 2 boxes of cornflakes and spends £3.44. Mr Brown buys 4 cartons of milk and 3 boxes of cornflakes and receives £6.03 change after paying with a £10 note. Write down a pair of simultaneous equations and solve them to find the price in pence of a carton of milk (*m*) and a box of cornflakes (*c*).

Q7 Solve $\frac{3(x - y)}{5} = x - 3y = x - 6$.

Direct and Inverse Proportion

Make sure you know the 4 main details about Direct and Inverse Proportion:
1) what happens to one quantity when the other increases,
2) what the graph looks like,
3) the table of values and
4) whether it's the ratio or the product that's the same for all values.

Q1 y is directly proportional to x. If $y = 5$ when x is 25, find y when x is 100.

Q2 y is directly proportional to x. If y is 1.2 when x is 2.5, find the value of y when $x = 3.75$.

Q3   Complete the following tables of values where y is always directly proportional to x.

a)

X	2	4	6
y	5	10	

b)

X	3	6	9
y		9	

c)

X	27		
y	5	10	15

Q4   If $y = 3$ when $x = 8$ and y is inversely proportional to x, find the value of y when $x = 12$.

Q5   If y and x vary inversely, and $y = 12$ when $x = 3$, find:
a) the value of x when $y = 9$
b) the value of y when $x = 6$.

Q6   The length of a squid is directly proportional to the number of raccoons it has eaten.
A squid 890 cm long was found to have eaten 58 raccoons in its lifetime. Calculate:
a) the length of squid that had eaten 29 raccoons
b) the number of raccoons that a 614 cm long squid has eaten.

Q7   Some scientists are building a telescope to view a space dragon. They know the length is
proportional to the magnification and calculate that a telescope 3 metres long will make
the dragon appear 50 times larger. How long would it need to be to make the dragon:
a) appear 75 times larger?
b) appear 220 times larger?
c) They find the space dragon looks too scary so close-up.
How long does the telescope need to be to make the dragon appear 15 times larger?

Q8   If $y \propto x$ and $y = 132$ when $x = 10$, find the value of y when $x = 14$.

Q9   If $y \propto x$ and $y = 117$ when $x = 45$, find the value of x when $y = 195$.

Q10   If $y \propto \dfrac{1}{x}$ and $x = 4$ when $y = 5$, find the value of x when $y = 10$.

Q11   Given that $y \propto \dfrac{1}{x}$, complete this table of values.

x	1	2	3	4	5	6
y					9.6	

Put the numbers into the equation $y = k/x$ to find the value of k. Then you can find the rest of the ys.

Direct and Inverse Proportion

Q12 If $y \propto x^2$ and $y = 4$ when $x = 4$, find the value of y when $x = 12$.

Q13 $y = kx^3$ and $y = 200$ when $x = 5$.
a) Find the value of k.
b) Find the value of y when $x = 8$.
c) Find the value of x when $y = 2433.4$.

Q14 In each of the tables of values below, y varies inversely with the square of x. Complete the tables, given that x is always positive.

a)

x	1	2	5	
y			4	1

b)

x	2			8
y	24	6	2⅔	

Q15 Two cylindrical containers are filled to the same depth, d cm, with water. The mass of the water in each container is proportional to the square of the radius of each container. The first container has a radius of 16 cm and the water has a mass of 16 kg. If the second container has a radius of 8 cm, find the mass of the water inside it.

d cm   r = 16 cm

d cm   r = 8 cm

Q16 If r varies inversely with the square of s, and $r = 24$ when $s = 10$, find the values of:
a) r when $s = 5$
b) s when $r = 150$, given that s is positive
c) r when $s = 2$
d) s when $r = 37\frac{1}{2}$, given that s is negative

 Don't forget about that little joker, the "inverse square" variation — they'll expect you to know that, too.

Q17 The gravitational pull of the Earth is inversely proportional to the square of the distance from the centre of the Earth. At the Earth's surface (approx. 6371 km from the centre) the gravitational pull is around 9.8 N kg⁻¹. When launching a satellite into space, the gravitational pull helps determine the orbit. What would be the gravitational pull on a satellite at a height of 100 km above the Earth's surface (to 1 d.p)?

Q18 By considering the values in the table, decide whether $y \propto x$, $y \propto \frac{1}{x}$ or $y \propto \frac{1}{x^2}$.

a) Write down an equation which shows how y varies with x.
b) Find the value of y when $x = 6.4$
c) Find the value of x when $y = 16$.

x	1.2	2.5	3.2	4.8
y	166⅔	80	62.5	41⅔

Quadratics

Q1 Factorise the quadratics first, and then solve the equations:

a) $x^2 + 3x - 10 = 0$
b) $x^2 - 5x + 6 = 0$
c) $x^2 - 2x + 1 = 0$

d) $x^2 - 4x + 3 = 0$
e) $x^2 - x - 20 = 0$
f) $x^2 - 4x - 5 = 0$

g) $x^2 + 6x - 7 = 0$
h) $x^2 + 14x + 49 = 0$
i) $x^2 - 2x - 15 = 0$.

Q2 Rearrange into the form "$x^2 + bx + c = 0$", then solve by factorising:

a) $x^2 + 6x = 16$

b) $x^2 + 5x = 36$

c) $x^2 + 4x = 45$

d) $x^2 = 5x$

e) $x^2 = 11x$

f) $x^2 - 21 = 4x$

g) $x^2 - 300 = 20x$

h) $x^2 + 48 = 26x$

i) $x^2 + 36 = 13x$

j) $x + 5 - \dfrac{14}{x} = 0$

k) $x + 4 - \dfrac{21}{x} = 0$

l) $x(x - 3) = 10$

m) $x^2 - 3(x + 6) = 0$

n) $x - \dfrac{63}{x} = 2$

o) $x + 1 = \dfrac{12}{x}$

Q3 Solve $x^2 - \dfrac{1}{4} = 0$.

Q4 The area of a rectangular swimming pool is 28 m². The width is x m. The difference between the length and width is 3 m. Find the value of x.

x m

Q5 A rug has length x m. The width is exactly 1 m less than the length.

x m

a) Write down an expression for the area of the rug.
b) If the area of the rug is 6 m², find the value of x.

Q6 A triangle has height $(x + 1)$ cm and a base of $2x$ cm.

a) Write down an expression for the area of the triangle and simplify it.
b) If the area of the triangle is 12 cm², find the value of x.

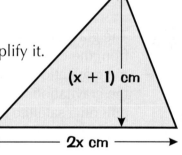

(x + 1) cm

2x cm

Q7 A square room has a floor of sides x metres. The height of the walls is 3 m. Write down an expression for:

a) the floor area
b) the area of all four walls.
c) If the total area of the floor and the four walls is 64 m², form a quadratic equation and solve it to find x.

Quadratics

Q8   Find the two values, to 2 d.p, given by each of the following expressions:

a) $\dfrac{2 \pm \sqrt{3}}{2}$

b) $\dfrac{4 \pm \sqrt{10}}{3}$

c) $\dfrac{-2 \pm \sqrt{27}}{2}$

d) $\dfrac{-3 \pm \sqrt{42}}{3}$

e) $\dfrac{-10 \pm \sqrt{160}}{5}$

f) $\dfrac{-27 \pm \sqrt{10}}{2}$

g) $\dfrac{-8 \pm \sqrt{9.5}}{2.4}$

h) $\dfrac{10 \pm \sqrt{88.4}}{23.2}$

Q9   The following quadratics can be solved by factorisation, but practise using the formula to solve them.

a) $x^2 + 8x + 12 = 0$
b) $6x^2 - x - 2 = 0$
c) $x^2 - x - 6 = 0$
d) $x^2 - 3x + 2 = 0$
e) $4x^2 - 15x + 9 = 0$
f) $x^2 - 3x = 0$
g) $36x^2 - 48x + 16 = 0$
h) $3x^2 + 8x = 0$
i) $2x^2 - 7x - 4 = 0$

j) $x^2 + x - 20 = 0$
k) $4x^2 + 8x - 12 = 0$
l) $3x^2 - 11x - 20 = 0$
m) $x + 3 = 2x^2$
n) $5 - 3x - 2x^2 = 0$
o) $1 - 5x + 6x^2 = 0$
p) $3(x^2 + 2x) = 9$
q) $x^2 + 4(x - 3) = 0$
r) $x^2 = 2(4 - x)$

> **Step number 1...**
> Write out the formula.

> **Step number 2...**
> Write down values for a, b and c.

> **Step number 3...** sub a, b and c into the formula. Make sure you divide the <u>whole</u> of the top line by <u>2a</u> — not just ½ of it.

Q10   Solve the following quadratics using the formula.
Give your answers to no more than two decimal places.

a) $x^2 + 3x - 1 = 0$
b) $x^2 - 2x - 6 = 0$
c) $x^2 + x - 1 = 0$
d) $x^2 + 6x + 3 = 0$
e) $x^2 + 5x + 2 = 0$
f) $x^2 - x - 1 = 0$
g) $3x^2 + 10x - 8 = 0$

h) $x^2 + 4x + 2 = 0$
i) $x^2 - 6x - 8 = 0$
j) $x^2 - 14x + 11 = 0$
k) $x^2 + 3x - 5 = 0$
l) $7x^2 - 15x + 6 = 0$
m) $2x^2 + 6x - 3 = 0$
n) $2x^2 - 7x + 4 = 0$

Q11   Rearrange the following in the form "$ax^2 + bx + c = 0$" and then solve by the quadratic formula. Give your answers to two decimal places.

a) $x^2 = 8 - 3x$

b) $(x + 2)^2 - 3 = 0$

c) $3x(x - 1) = 5$

d) $2x(x + 4) = 1$

e) $x^2 = 4(x + 1)$

f) $(2x - 1)^2 = 5$

g) $3x^2 + 2x = 6$

h) $(x + 2)(x + 3) = 5$

i) $(x - 2)(2x - 1) = 3$

j) $2x + \dfrac{4}{x} = 7$

k) $\left(x - \dfrac{1}{2}\right)^2 = \dfrac{1}{4}$

l) $4x(x - 2) = -3$

Oops, forgot to mention step number 4...
check your answers by putting them <u>back in the equation.</u>

Quadratics

Q12 The sides of a right angled triangle are as shown. Use Pythagoras' theorem to form a quadratic equation in x and then solve it to find x.

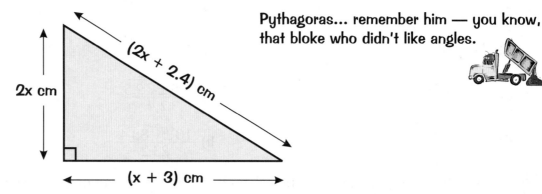

Pythagoras... remember him — you know, that bloke who didn't like angles.

2x cm

$(2x + 2.4)$ cm

$(x + 3)$ cm

Q13 The area of a rectangle with length $(x + 4.6)$ cm and width $(x - 2.1)$ cm is 134.63 cm².

a) Form a quadratic equation and solve it to find x to two decimal places.

b) What is the rectangle's perimeter to one decimal place?

$(x - 2.1)$ cm

$(x + 4.6)$ cm

Q14 Complete the square for the following expressions:

a) $x^2 - 4x - 5$

b) $x^2 - 2x + 1$

c) $x^2 + x + 1$

d) $x^2 - 6x + 9$

e) $x^2 - 6x + 7$

f) $x^2 - 4x$

First look at what you need to put in the bracket to get the x^2 and x terms. Then work the number part out at the end.

g) $x^2 + 3x - 4$

h) $x^2 - x - 3$

i) $x^2 - 10x + 25$

j) $x^2 - 10x$

k) $x^2 + 8x + 17$

l) $x^2 - 12x + 35$

 All you're doing when completing the square is writing it in the form "$(x + 4)^2 + 2$" instead of "$x^2 + 8x + 18$" — don't let the name put you off.

Q15 Solve the following quadratic equations by completing the square. Write down your answers to no more than 2 d.p.

a) $x^2 + 3x - 1 = 0$

b) $x^2 - x - 3 = 0$

c) $x^2 + 4x - 3 = 0$

d) $x^2 + x - 1 = 0$

e) $x^2 - 3x - 5 = 0$

f) $2x^2 - 6x + 1 = 0$

g) $3x^2 - 3x - 2 = 0$

h) $3x^2 - 6x - 1 = 0$

It's quite a cunning method, really... but I admit it takes a bit of getting used to — make sure you've learnt all the steps, then it's just practice, practice...

Functions

Right, functions. Don't let appearances deceive you — treat them like the regular equations that you've seen loads of times before. Nothing to worry about here then.

Q1 Express the following equations using function notation:

a) $y = 3 + x$ **b)** $y = 790 - 41x$ **c)** $y = 3(9x^2 + 2)$

Q2 For the following functions find x when $f(x) = 2$:

a) $f(x) = 2x - 7$ **c)** $f(x) = 5 - 4x \times 8x$ **e)** $f(x) = x^2 + 7x$
b) $f(x) = x^2 + 1$ **d)** $f(x) = 3x^2 - 10$ **f)** $f(x) = 252 - 2x^3$

Q3 For the following functions find $f(5)$:

a) $f(x) = x + 7 - 3$ **c)** $f(x) = 18 - x^2 + 9x$ **e)** $f(x) = 121x \div 11x^2$
b) $f(x) = x^2 + x$ **d)** $f(x) = (72 - 7) \div x$ **f)** $f(x) = 4(x + x^3)$

Q4 If $f(x) = 4x + 12$ and $g(x) = 3 - x^2$ then find:

a) $f(8)$ **c)** $f(-4)$ **e)** $fg(x)$
b) $g(3)$ **d)** $gf(x)$ **f)** $gf(2)$

Q5 If $f(x) = 6 - 2x$, $g(x) = \dfrac{9}{x}$ and $h(x) = 6 + x^2$ then find:

a) $f(-1)$ **c)** $fh(x)$ **e)** $fg(12)$
b) $g(1/3)$ **d)** $gf(x)$ **f)** $hf(-9)$

Q6 If $f(x) = \dfrac{11}{x + 1}$, $g(x) = \dfrac{3x}{4}$ and $h(x) = 6 + x$ then find:

a) $h^{-1}(x)$ **c)** $g^{-1}(h(x))$ **e)** $h^{-1}(f(5))$
b) $f^{-1}(x)$ **d)** $f^{-1}(g(x))$ **f)** $h^{-1}(g(-1))$

Q7 Evaluate the following:

a) $f(-1)$ where $f(x) = \dfrac{2 + 4x}{3}$ **d)** $n^{-1}(2)$ where $n(x) = 32 + 4(-x + 7)$

b) $g(9)$ where $g(x) = 7x^2 - 13$ **e)** $t{:}x \longrightarrow 21 - x^2$ where $x = 3$

c) $kj(-3)$ where $j(x) = \dfrac{6(x - 2)}{2}$ and $k(x) = -14x$ **f)** $v{:}x \longrightarrow -\dfrac{3x}{12}$ where $x = 3$

Q8 Find:

a) $hi(x)$, if $h(x) = \dfrac{11}{x} - 8$ and $i(x) = \dfrac{x^2 - x}{2}$

b) $m^{-1}(x)$, if $m(x) = \dfrac{18x - 12}{10} + 3$

c) $p^{-1}(q(x))$, if $p(x) = 8x + 5$ and $q(x) = \dfrac{13}{x - 2}$

Inequalities

Yet another one of those bits of Maths that looks worse than it is —
these are just like equations, really, except for the symbols.

Q1 Write down the inequality represented by each diagram below.

a)

b)

> On a number line, a closed
> (or filled-in) circle means
> the inequality is ≤ or ≥,
> and an open (or empty)
> circle means it's < or >.

c)

d)

e)

f)

g)

h)

Q2 By drawing an appropriate part of the number line for each question, represent each of
the following inequalities.

a) $5 < x$ **c)** $-5 < x < 2$ **e)** $-2 \leq x < 3$ **g)** $-3 \leq x \leq -2$

b) $x \leq 2$ **d)** $-2 < x \leq 3$ **f)** $6 \leq x < 7$ **h)** $-3 \leq x < 0$

Q3 Draw and label a number line from –5 to 5 for each of the following questions.
Represent the inequalities on your number lines.

a) $x^2 \leq 4$ **c)** $x^2 \leq 9$ **e)** $16 \geq x^2$ **g)** $9 > x^2$

b) $x^2 < 1$ **d)** $25 \geq x^2$ **f)** $x^2 \leq 1$ **h)** $x^2 \leq 0$

Q4 Solve the following:

a) $3x + 2 > 11$ **e)** $2x - 7 \geq 8$ **i)** $5(x + 2) \geq 25$ **m)** $8 - 3x \geq 14$

b) $5x + 4 < 24$ **f)** $17 + 4x < 33$ **j)** $4(x - 1) > 40$ **n)** $16 - x < 11$

c) $5x + 7 \leq 32$ **g)** $2(x + 3) < 20$ **k)** $10 - 2x > 4x - 8$ **o)** $16 - x > 1$

d) $3x + 12 \leq 30$ **h)** $2(5x - 4) < 32$ **l)** $7 - 2x \leq 4x + 10$ **p)** $12 - 3x \leq 18$

Inequalities

Q5 Find the largest integer x, such that $2x + 5 \geq 5x - 2$.

Q6 When a number is subtracted from 11, and this new number is then divided by two, the result is always less than five. Write this information as an inequality and solve it to show the possible values of the number.

Q7 Two schools are merging and a new school is being built to accommodate all the pupils. There will be 1,130 pupils in total in the new school. No class must have more than 32 pupils. Show this information as an inequality. How many classrooms are needed?

Call the number of classrooms x.

Q8 A couple are planning their wedding. For the reception in a local hotel, they have a budget of £900. If the hotel charges £18 per head, how many guests could be invited? Show this information as an inequality.

Q9 The central unshaded region satisfies three inequalities. Write down these inequalities.

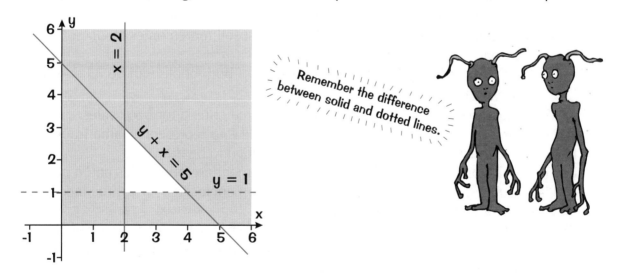

Remember the difference between solid and dotted lines.

Q10 Draw a set of axes with the x-axis from –2 to 6 and the y-axis from –1 to 7. Show on a graph the region enclosed by the following three inequalities.

$$y < 6, \qquad x + y \geq 5 \qquad \text{and} \qquad x \leq 5$$

Q11 Draw a set of axes with the x-axis from –4 to 5 and the y-axis from –3 to 6. Show on a graph the region enclosed by the following.

$$y \leq 2x + 4, \qquad y < 5 - x \qquad \text{and} \qquad y \geq \frac{x}{3} - 1$$

Using Graphical Inequalities

Q1 Sarah has a maximum of £100 to spend on books and DVDs. Books cost £5 each, DVDs cost £10 each. She must buy more DVDs than books. She must buy at least 5 books.

a) Write three inequalities to show her constraints.

b) Draw a graph to show these inequalities.
Put books (B) on the horizontal axis and DVDs (C) on the vertical axis.

c) Write the letter X in the region which satisfies the inequalities.

d) Write down all of the solutions which satisfy these inequalities.

Q2 Mr Smith has a maximum of £10 000 to spend on machinery.
He has a choice of two types of machine. Machine A costs £200,
machine B costs £500. He must buy at least 40 machines.

a) Write two inequalities to describe his constraints.

b) Draw a graph to show these inequalities.
Put machine A on the horizontal axis and machine B on the vertical axis.

c) Write the letter X in the region which satisfies the inequalities.

d) Machine A produces 4 items per day, machine B produces 11 items per day.
Mr Smith wants to maximise output.
  i)   How many machines of type A should he purchase?
  ii) How many machines of type B should he purchase?
  iii) What is the maximum number of items which can be produced in a day?

Q3 The local bookshop is about to start selling two new books: "Giant Mechanical Legs" and "Llama Trauma". The sales of these books is limited by the following factors:
  1. Supply of Llama Trauma is restricted to 30 copies a month.
  2. The publisher insists that the bookshop must sell more copies of Giant Mechanical Legs than of Llama Trauma.
  3. Shelf space is limited so that the total sales of both books will be 75 or fewer copies a month.

a) Write out three inequalities to represent the three criteria for book sales.
Use *G* to represent "Giant Mechanical Legs and *L* to represent "Llama Trauma".

b) What are the two extra conditions that don't need to be drawn?

c) The bookshop wants to find the optimum income these book sales could produce.
Using suitable axes, show on a graph the region enclosed by the three inequalities where they could find this information.

d) Given than a copy of "Giant Mechanical Legs" costs £4.50 and a copy of "Llama Trauma" costs £7.30 find the maximum possible income and how many of each book would need to be sold in a month to achieve it.

Q4 Edwin buys a travel card to use on buses and trams.
The restrictions on its use are written on the card:

a) Write out three inequalities to represent the travel card restrictions. Use *T* for the number of tram rides and use *B* for the number of bus rides.

b) Using suitable axes, draw a graph to show these inequalities.

Uberville Public Transport

Restrictions:
1) No more than 12 tram rides
2) No more tram rides than bus rides
3) Number of bus rides allowed is three times those taken by tram.

HandyCard

c) Edwin wants to work out the maximum amount he can save by using the travel card.
Without a travel card a bus ride costs £1.20 and a tram ride costs £4.00.
Find the combination of tram and bus rides which saves the most money.

Symmetry

They do say that bad things happen in threes... and now you've got to learn three types of symmetry — but don't worry, I reckon their names pretty much give the game away.

There are THREE types of symmetry:	
1) LINE SYMMETRY	You can draw a mirror line across the object and both sides will fold together exactly.
2) PLANE SYMMETRY	This applies to 3D solids. You can draw a plane mirror surface through the solid to make the shape exactly the same on both sides of the plane.
3) ROTATIONAL SYMMETRY	You can rotate the shape or drawing into different positions that all look exactly the same.

Q1 Draw <u>all</u> the lines of symmetry for each of the following shapes.
(Some shapes may have no lines of symmetry)

a)   b)   c)   d)   e)   f)

These questions are a piece of cake if you use tracing paper — and remember you can use it in the Exam, so take some with you or ask for it.

Q2 What is the <u>order of rotational symmetry</u> for each of the following shapes?

a)   b)   c)   d)

Q3 Mark in the <u>lines of symmetry</u> of the following letters.
State the <u>order</u> of rotational symmetry for each one.

MHVAKSZ

Q4 Draw an example of each of the following shapes. Put in the <u>lines of symmetry</u> and state the <u>order</u> of rotational symmetry.

a) An equilateral triangle.
b) An isosceles triangle.
c) A rhombus.
d) An isosceles trapezium.
e) A regular octagon.
f) A parallelogram.

Symmetry

Watch out for those 3D solids and planes of symmetry — they're pretty hard to draw, so make sure you do this page in pencil — and have a rubber ready...

Q5 On each cube draw in a different <u>plane of symmetry</u>.

Q6 Here is a cuboid:

Is this plane a plane of symmetry?

Q7 How many planes of symmetry does this <u>triangular prism</u> have?

Q8 How many planes of symmetry does a <u>circular cone</u> have?

Q9 In the square-based pyramid shown, is this a plane of symmetry?

Q10 Draw in another plane of symmetry, which is <u>perpendicular</u> to the one drawn in the diagram.

Q11 How many planes of symmetry does a <u>tetrahedron</u> have?

Q12 Would all the planes of symmetry of a cube meet at a <u>line</u>, <u>point</u> or <u>plane</u>?

Polygons

The one thing they're <u>guaranteed</u> to ask you about is <u>Interior and Exterior Angles</u> — you'd better get learning those formulas...

A <u>POLYGON</u> is a many-sided shape. A <u>REGULAR</u> polygon is one where <u>ALL THE SIDES AND ANGLES ARE THE SAME</u>.

You need to know these two formulas:

1) EXTERIOR ANGLE = 360° ÷ No. of Sides

2) INTERIOR ANGLE = 180° – EXTERIOR ANGLE

Q1   What sort of triangles occur in every <u>regular polygon</u> (<u>except</u> a hexagon), when each vertex is joined to the centre by a straight line?

Q2   Using a compass, construct an <u>equilateral</u> triangle with sides of 3 cm. What is the interior angle at each vertex?

Q3   Sketch a regular hexagon and draw in all its lines of symmetry. State the order of <u>rotational</u> symmetry.

Q4   A square and a regular hexagon are placed adjacent to each other.
a) What is the size of ∠PQW?
b) What is the size of ∠PRW?
c) How many sides has the regular polygon that has ∠PQW as one of its angles?

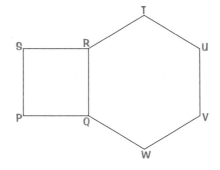

Q5   a) The <u>sum</u> of the <u>interior</u> angles of a <u>regular</u> 24-sided polygon is 3960°. Use this to calculate the size of one <u>interior</u> angle.
b) From your answer to part a) calculate one <u>exterior</u> angle and show that the <u>sum</u> of the exterior angles equals 360°.

Q6

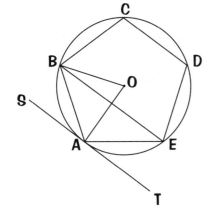

ABCDE is a regular pentagon. It is drawn in a circle centre O. SAT is a tangent drawn to the circle at A.
a) Calculate the size of angle BOA.
b) Find the size of angle OBA.
c) Write down the size of angle:
   i)   SAO
   ii) BAS.
d) Write down the size of angle BEA giving a reason for your answer.

Polygons

Q7 The sum of the interior angles of a regular polygon is 2520°. How many sides does this regular polygon have?

Remember that formula for the sum of interior angles — it comes in handy here.

Q8

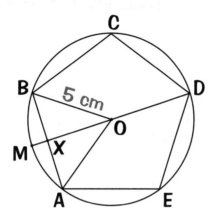

ABCDE is a regular pentagon whose vertices lie on a circle of radius 5 cm, centre O. DOM is an axis of symmetry of the pentagon and cuts the chord AB at X.

a) Calculate the size of angle BOX.

b) Find the length OX. Hence find the distance of M from the chord AB.

You need to use trigonometry to find OX — Cos θ = adj / hyp.

Q9 ABCDEFGH is a regular octagon.

a) Copy the figure and mark on the axis of symmetry which maps H to A.

b) Calculate the size of angle EFC.

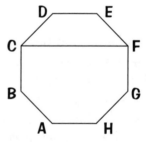

Q10 In each of the pentagons below, all the sides are of equal length, two of the angles are 90° and the other interior angles are m, m, and r degrees.

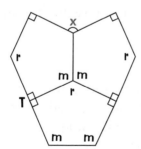

a) Explain in two different ways why 2m + r = 360°.

b) What is the size of angle x?

c) Copy the diagram and add two more pentagons (by tracing through) so that the point T is completely surrounded and the whole figure forms part of a tessellation. Label all the angles of the new pentagons.

Q11 An <u>irregular pentagon</u> has interior angles of 100°, 104°, 120°. If the other two angles are equal, what is their size?

Perimeters and Areas

Q1   Calculate the area and perimeter of the rectangle.

Q2   Calculate the area and perimeter of the square.

Q3   An attachment on a child's toy is made from plastic in the shape of an octagon with a square cut out. A diagram of the attachment is shown on the right. By counting squares or otherwise, find the area of plastic needed to make 4 of these attachments.

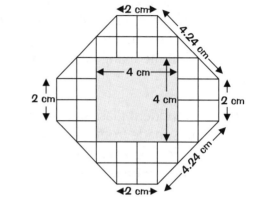

Q4   A rectangular dining room, with a width equal to half its length, needs carpet tiling.
   a) Calculate the area of the floor, if its width is 12 m.
   b) If carpet tiles are 50 cm by 50 cm squares, calculate how many tiles will be required.
   c) If carpet tiles cost £4.99 per m^2, calculate the <u>cost</u> of tiling the dining room.

Q5   Josh is making a cube-shaped bean bag out of material for his textiles coursework. To make each side of the cube he needs a square of material with edges of length 60 cm. How many <u>square metres</u> of material will Josh need?

Q6   Natasha is training for a marathon by jogging around the outside of a square field of area 9000 m^2. One evening, Natasha completed 11 laps of the field. How far did she run? Give your answer to the nearest 100 m.

Q7   A rectangular lawn is to be made 48 m^2. If its width is 5 m, how long is it? How many rolls of turf 50 cm wide and 11 m long should be ordered to grass this area?

Q8   This parallelogram has an area of 4773 mm^2. How long is its <u>base</u>?

Q9   A metal blade for a craft knife is the shape of a <u>trapezium</u>. Calculate the area of the metal.

 If you can't remember the formula for the area of a trapezium, you can always split the shape into a rectangle and a triangle.

SECTION FIVE — SHAPES, AREAS AND DRAWING

Perimeters and Areas

Q10 Jon is making a metal bracket as part of his technology project.
The bracket is stamped out of sheet metal in a 2 phase process:
1st: The <u>outer triangle</u>, measuring 14.4 cm by 10 cm,
is stamped out.
2nd: A smaller <u>inner triangle</u> measuring 5.76 cm by 4 cm
is stamped out of the larger triangle.
The bracket should be made from no more than 50 cm²
of sheet metal if the fixing is to support its weight.
Will the fixing take the weight of Jon's bracket?

Q11 A modern glass sculpture is to be erected.
It is made from glass in the shape of two mountain peaks.
Calculate each <u>separate</u> area and hence
find the <u>total</u> area of glass required.

Q12

All measurements in m

You have been asked to paint the outside wall
of a building shown in the diagram opposite.

a) Find the area of wall that needs painting.
b) A 1 litre tin of paint will cover 13 m².
How many 1 litre tins are needed to
give the wall two coats of paint?
c) The wall is also going to have a tiled
border around the edge. Calculate the
length of the edge of the wall to be tiled.

You need the two
circle formulas here
— $C = \pi \times d$ and
$A = \pi \times r^2$.

Q13 A fighter aircraft's wing is shown on the right.
Calculate its <u>area</u>, and its <u>perimeter</u>.

Two lots of Pythagoras are needed
to find the length of the third side.

Q14 A simple tent is to be made in the shape of a
triangular prism. The dimensions are shown
in the diagram.
  a) The two end faces are isosceles triangles.
  Find their areas.
  b) The two sides and ground sheet are
  rectangles. Find their areas.
  c) How much material is required to make
  this tent?

Q15 Calculate the area of a <u>rhombus</u> with diagonals 7 km and 11 km.

Solids and Nets

Before you go any further — make sure you know these 3 facts...

Surface Area and Nets

1) <u>SURFACE AREA</u> only applies to solid 3D objects. It's the <u>TOTAL AREA</u> of all the <u>OUTER SURFACES</u> added together.
2) A <u>NET</u> is just A <u>SOLID SHAPE</u> folded out <u>FLAT</u>.
3) SURFACE AREA OF SOLID = AREA OF NET.

There are 4 nets that you need to know inside out... so to speak:
1) <u>Triangular Prism</u>, 2) <u>Cube</u>, 3) <u>Cuboid</u>, 4) <u>Pyramid</u>. I reckon you shouldn't read any further till you're 100% happy with them.

Q1 The net shown will fold to make a cube. Only one flap is shown. <u>Copy</u> the diagram.

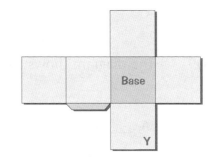

a) Put an X in each corner that touches Y when the cube is made up.
b) Put an F where the flap will join one face to another when the cube is made up.
c) Put on the other flaps necessary to glue the cube together.

Q2 Draw an <u>accurate</u> net that would fold to make the 3D cuboid shown (diagram is not full size). It is not necessary to include flaps.

Q3 Draw a <u>full size net</u> (without flaps) of a square-based pyramid whose base has sides of length 3 cm.

Q4 Julie is designing new packaging boxes for her home-made jewellery. Draw <u>accurately</u> the net of a triangular-based pyramid, with sufficient flaps to glue it together.

Q5 a) What shape is the <u>base</u> of the cuboid shown opposite?
b) Which edges are the same length as DE?
c) Which lengths equal CE?
d) Which lengths equal the diagonal DG?
e) How many vertices does the cuboid have?

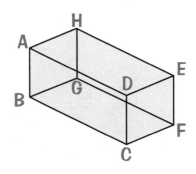

Q6 Draw a <u>circular cone</u>.
a) How many vertices does it have?
b) How many edges?

Solids and Nets

Q7 An equilateral triangular prism has a triangular-based pyramid placed on top of it, as shown. For this <u>combined</u> solid,

    a) How many edges does it have?

    b) How many vertices?

    c) How many faces?

Q8

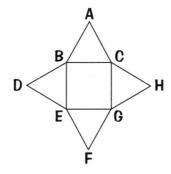

The diagram shows the net of a solid in which ABC is an equilateral triangle and BCGE is a square.

    a) Which points will coincide with A when the net is folded up to make the solid?

    b) Describe the symmetry of the net.

    c) How many faces, edges and vertices does it have when in solid form?

Q9 The diagram shows the net of a cube of edge 8 cm.

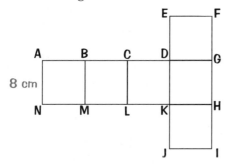

    a) Which point coincides with M when the net is folded to make the cube?

    b) Find the area of the face DGHK.

    c) What is the total surface area of the cube?

Q10

This diagram shows a net for a rectangular box with a lid. For the same box sketch a different net.

Q11 Which of these two nets will form a pyramid on a triangular base with all four faces equilateral triangles?

Net A

Net B

Q12

The diagram shows part of the net of a triangular prism.

    a) Copy and complete the net.

        It is not necessary to include flaps.

    b) What is the surface area of the prism?

SECTION FIVE — SHAPES, AREAS AND DRAWING

Surface Area and Volume

Make sure you know all the <u>volume formulas</u> you need.

Q1 Joe buys a polythene tunnel to protect his plants from frost. It has a semicircular diameter of 70 cm and a length of 3 m.

a) Find the cross-sectional area.

b) Hence find the volume of the tunnel.

3 m

70 cm

Q2 I am planning to build a circular pond in my garden surrounded by a ring shaped paved area. The pond will be 50 cm deep and filled with water.

a) Calculate the approximate cost of paving the area around the pond with slabs costing £16 per m². Give your answer to the nearest £10.

b) I need to add 15 ml of liquid pond treatment for every m³ of water in the pond. Find the volume of treatment I will need to add to the pond. Give your answer to the nearest ml.

paved area

4 m

5 m

Q3 A solid metal cube, each of whose sides is 10 cm long, is melted down and made into a solid cylinder 10 cm high.

a) What is the radius of this cylinder?

b) Find the surface area of the cylinder.

10 cm

10 cm

10 cm

10 cm

Q4

a) A tin mug has the dimensions shown. What is the greatest volume of milk the mug can hold?

b) In fact, 600 cm³ of milk is poured in. How high will it go up the mug?

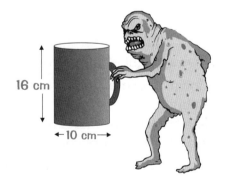

16 cm

←10 cm→

Q5

3 cm

3 cm

5 mm

A nut has the cross-section illustrated. The circular hole has a diameter of 1.4 cm and the nut is 5 mm thick. Find the volume of the nut in cm³.

(Units...)

Surface Area and Volume

Q6 Steve has bought a pair of speaker stands. The base of each stand is a hollow prism with the dimensions shown. A hollow tube of diameter 4 cm and height 110 cm screws into the top of each base to form the stand.

Steve is filling the stands with sand to improve stability. Find the volume of sand Steve needs to use to fill both stands (the bases *and* the tubes). Give your answer in litres to 2 d.p.

1 litre = 1000 cm³

Q7

Jill buys a bookshelf with the dimensions shown in the diagram.
a) Find the cross-sectional area.
b) Find the volume of the bookshelf in m³.

Q8 Bill has a greenhouse with dimensions as shown. The roof is made up of eight panels of equal size.

A storm breaks all of the glass in the shaded area on the diagram.

Calculate the area of glass which Bill must buy to repair his greenhouse.

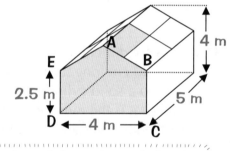

Look for a right-angled triangle to calculate AB.

Q9 A cuboid has a height of x m, a width of $(3 - x)$ m and a length of $(5 - x)$ m.

a) Write down an expression for the volume of the cuboid.
b) Complete the table of values using your expression for the volume of the cuboid.
c) Draw a graph of V against x for $0 \leqslant x \leqslant 3$.
d) Use your graph to estimate the maximum volume of the cuboid.
e) Estimate the surface area of the cuboid when the volume is at its maximum.
f) The actual volume of the cuboid is 6 m³.
By using your graph to find the two possible values of x, estimate the maximum total surface area of the cuboid for this volume.

x	0	1	2	3
V			6	

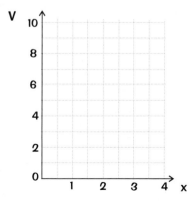

Surface Area and Volume

Here are some formulas that will come in handy for the next few questions:

r = radius

l = slant length

h = height

B = Area of base

P = perimeter of base

Shape	Surface Area	Volume
Sphere	$4\pi r^2$	$\frac{4}{3}\pi r^3$
Cone	$\pi r l$	$\frac{1}{3}\pi r^2 h$
Pyramid	$B + \frac{Pl}{2}$	$\frac{1}{3}Bh$

Q10

2.6 cm

1.8 cm

1.2 cm

An egg timer is symmetrical and consists of hemispheres, cylinders and cones joined together as shown to the left.

a) Calculate the volume of sand in the upper container.
(Hint: you need to find three volumes and add them together.)

Sand runs into the bottom container at a constant rate of 0.05 cm³ per second. At the end of a certain time period the sand has fallen through into the bottom container as shown to the right.

0.3 cm

1.2 cm

h

b) How high (h) has it risen up the cylindrical part of the bottom container?

c) How long has it taken the sand to fall through until it is at this height?

Q11

← 5 cm →

2 cm

10 cm

chocolate

4 cm

To make a 'Bandito's Barnetto', an ice-cream cone is used which is 10 cm deep and has a base diameter of 5 cm. The tip of the cone is filled 4 cm deep with solid chocolate as shown. The rest of the cone is filled with ice cream and a hemisphere of ice cream is mounted on top so that the base of the hemisphere coincides with the base of the cone.

a) Calculate the volume of ice cream required for just one Barnetto.

b) Calculate the outer surface area of the cone.

Q12

20 cm

10 cm

10 cm

Mike and Shelly are doing an experiment to find the radius of a marble. They fill a cylindrical container of diameter 10 cm and height 20 cm with water to a depth of 10 cm. 200 identical marbles are now submerged in the water. The depth increases to 14.5 cm. Calculate the radius of one marble.

The volume increase is a cylinder and you're told the height.

Q13 Kaphiri is planning to build a square-based pyramid with dimensions as shown in the diagram.

a) What will be the volume of the completed pyramid?

b) What will the surface area of the whole pyramid be?

c) 1 litre of paint will cover 15 m². How much paint will Kaphiri need to paint the visible parts of the pyramid?

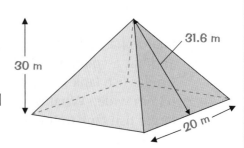

31.6 m

30 m

20 m

SECTION FIVE — SHAPES, AREAS AND DRAWING

Congruence, Similarity and Enlargements

Q1 Which pair of triangles are congruent? Explain why.

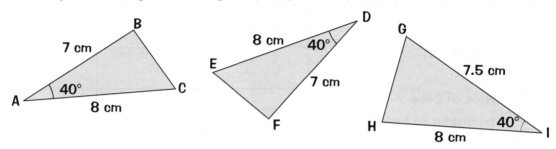

Q2 In the diagram below, BC is parallel to DE.
AB = 12 cm, BD = 8 cm, DE = 25 cm and CE = 10 cm.

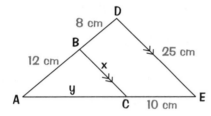

a) Explain why triangles ABC and ADE are similar.
b) Find the lengths of x and y in the diagram.

Q3 Another triangle, congruent to the triangle shown on the
right, must be drawn with vertices at three of the dots.
Show in how many different ways this can be done.

 Don't forget that when you're enlarging areas and volumes,
there's a bigger scale factor — that one catches everyone out.

Q4 Using the point O as centre of enlargement draw accurately and label:
a) the image $A_1B_1C_1$ of the triangle ABC after an enlargement
scale factor 2
b) the image $A_2B_2C_2$ of the triangle ABC after an enlargement
scale factor -1.
c) Which image is congruent to triangle ABC?

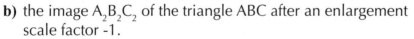

Q5 Sharon has a fish tank which is 42 cm wide
and has a volume of 30 litres. She sees a
similar fish tank in the pet shop which is
63 cm wide. What is the volume of the
larger fish tank to the nearest litre?

Congruence, Similarity and Enlargements

Q6 A cylindrical bottle can hold 1 litre of oil. A second cylindrical bottle has twice the radius but the same height. It also contains oil.
- **a)** Explain why these bottles are not similar.
- **b)** How much oil can the larger bottle hold?

Q7 A boy made a symmetrical framework with metal rods as shown. Lengths AB = BC, ST = TC and AP = PQ. Angle BVC = 90° and length BV = 9 cm.

- **a)** Find two triangles which are similar to triangle ABC.
- **b)** Calculate the length of AP. Hence find the length of PT.
- **c)** Calculate the area of triangle ABC.
- **d)** Find the area of triangle APQ. Give your answer correct to 3 significant figures.
- **e)** Hence find the area of PQBST correct to 2 significant figures.

Q8 For a graphics project, Eliza makes a model of a chocolate box in the shape of a cuboid 5 cm long, 2 cm wide and 3 cm high.

- **a)** Calculate the area of material needed to make the model (assuming no flaps are required for glueing).
- **b)** Eliza decides that the full size packaging will be similar to the model, but enlarged by a scale factor of 4. Calculate the area of material Eliza needs to make a full-size box.

Q9 On a holiday near the sea, some children built a sandcastle in the shape of a cone. The radius of the base is 100 cm and the height is 100 cm.

Volume of a cone:
$$\frac{1}{3}\pi r^2 h$$

- **a)** What is the volume of the sandcastle in m³ correct to 3 significant figures?

  The children now remove the top portion to make a similar cone that is 50 cm high.

- **b)** State the radius of the base of this smaller cone.
- **c)** State the ratio of the volume of the small cone to the volume of the original cone.
- **d)** Calculate the volume of the small cone in m³ correct to 3 significant figures.
- **e)** Hence write down the ratio of the volume of the portion left of the original cone to the smaller cone in the form n:1.

Loci and Construction

Don't let a silly word like <u>locus</u> put you off — there are <u>easy marks</u> to be had here, but you've got to do everything neatly, using a pencil, ruler and compasses.

Q1 Inside a 6 cm by 4 cm rectangle:

a) draw the locus of points 5 cm from D

b) draw the locus of points equidistant from A and D

c) indicate by an X, the point inside the rectangle which is 5 cm from D and equidistant from A and D.

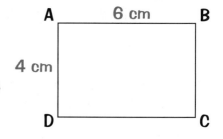

Q2 Construct triangle PQR accurately with length PQ = 10.5 cm, angle PQR = 95° and angle RPQ = 32°.

a) Construct the perpendicular bisector of the line PR. Draw in point A where the bisector crosses the line PQ.

b) Bisect angle PRQ. Draw in point B where the bisector crosses the line PQ. Measure the length BA.

Q3 Omar is doing some garden landscaping. Because of gas and water pipes, he is not allowed to dig anywhere within 3 m of his house.

Using a scale of 1 cm to 1 m, draw a diagram for Omar showing the walls of his house and the area in which he cannot dig.

Q4 Construct triangle PQR with length PQ = QR = 11.5 cm and angle PQR = 38°.

a) Construct the bisectors of angles QPR and QRP. Mark the point O where the 2 bisectors cross.

b) With centre O draw the circle which just touches the sides PQ, PR and QR of the triangle. What is the radius of this circle?

Q5 A and B are 2 points on a straight shore, 4 km apart with A due west of B.

a) Describe the locus of points P such that angle APB equals 90°.

b) Using a scale of 2 cm to 1 km draw an accurate scale diagram showing A, B, the shore line and the locus of P. An outcrop of rock is located on a bearing of 060° from A and 300° from B.

Think about your geometry rules.

c) Indicate the rock on your diagram. Mark the spot with an X.

d) A ship steaming due east parallel to the shore avoids the rock by following the locus of P. How near does the ship come to the rock?

Loci and Construction

Just to be really awkward, these points don't always make a nice line — they can cover a whole area... and you're gonna be asked to shade areas containing all the points.

Q6   This is a plan of Simon's room.

To keep warm Simon must be within 2 m of the wall with the radiator on. To see out of the window he must be within 1.5 m of the wall containing the window.

a) Using a scale of 2 cm to 1 m draw a plan of Simon's room.

b) Shade the region in which Simon must be if he is to be warm and see out of the window.

Q7   A running track is designed so that each point on the track is 32.5 m from a fixed line AB which is 100 m long.

a) Draw the locus of the track.

b) Calculate the distance once round the running track.

Q8   Jim is landscaping his back garden, and has drawn the plan below. Two sides of the garden are bounded by fences and the other sides are bounded by the walls of the house and garage. The garden is in the shape of a rectangle.

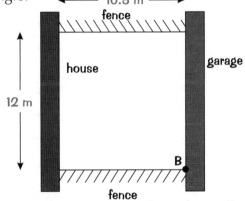

a) Using a scale of 1 cm to 1 m draw a plan of Jim's garden.

b) Ben, the family dog, will be tethered to the garage at B by a lead of length 6 m. Construct accurately and shade the part of the garden where Ben can go.

c) Jim wants to plant a tree in the garden. The tree must be planted more than 5 m away from the walls of the house and more than 4 m away from each fence. It must also be out of reach of Ben, and be more than 2 m away from the walls of the garage. On your plan of the garden, construct accurately and shade the region where Jim can plant his tree.

Q9   The positions of two islands A and B are found from the following information: A is 35 km from a jetty J on a bearing 065°, B is due south of A and on a bearing of 132° from J as shown below.

a) Using a scale of 1 cm to 5 km, draw an accurate plan to show the positions of J, A and B.

b) Find from your drawing the distance in km between the islands A and B.

c) A boat leaves the jetty at 09.00 and reaches A at 11.30. What is its average speed in km/h?

d) A lightship L is 20 km from J, equidistant from A and B and on the same side of J as A and B. Mark L on the drawing.

e) Find the bearing of L from J.

Vectors

Q1   ABCDE is a pentagon.

$$\overrightarrow{AB} = \begin{pmatrix} 3 \\ 3 \end{pmatrix} \quad \overrightarrow{AC} = \begin{pmatrix} 2 \\ 6 \end{pmatrix} \quad \overrightarrow{AD} = \begin{pmatrix} -2 \\ 6 \end{pmatrix} \quad \overrightarrow{AE} = \begin{pmatrix} -3 \\ 2 \end{pmatrix}$$

a) Draw this pentagon accurately.

b) Write down the vectors:

    i) $\overrightarrow{DE}$ **ii)** $\overrightarrow{DC}$ **iii)** $\overrightarrow{EC}$

c) What sort of triangle is $\triangle$ ACD?

Q2 $\underset{\sim}{p} = \begin{pmatrix} 2 \\ 3 \end{pmatrix}, \underset{\sim}{q} = \begin{pmatrix} 0 \\ -2 \end{pmatrix}, \underset{\sim}{r} = \begin{pmatrix} 3 \\ -1 \end{pmatrix}, \underset{\sim}{s} = \begin{pmatrix} -1 \\ -2 \end{pmatrix}$

Calculate then draw:

a) $\underset{\sim}{p} + \underset{\sim}{q}$ **c)** $2\underset{\sim}{r}$ **e)** $2\underset{\sim}{p} - 2\underset{\sim}{s}$ **g)** $2\underset{\sim}{r} - \underset{\sim}{q}$ **i)** $\underset{\sim}{p} + 2\underset{\sim}{s}$

b) $\underset{\sim}{p} - \underset{\sim}{q}$ **d)** $\underset{\sim}{s} + \underset{\sim}{p}$ **f)** $3\underset{\sim}{q} + \underset{\sim}{s}$ **h)** $\frac{1}{2}\underset{\sim}{q} + 2\underset{\sim}{r}$ **j)** $\underset{\sim}{q} - 2\underset{\sim}{r}$

Q3

ABCD is a parallelogram. M, N, P and Q are the mid-points of the sides, as shown. $\overrightarrow{MQ} = \underset{\sim}{x}$ and $\overrightarrow{AM} = \underset{\sim}{y}$.

Express in terms of $\underset{\sim}{x}$ and $\underset{\sim}{y}$:

a) $\overrightarrow{AB}$ **c)** $\overrightarrow{NB}$ **e)** $\overrightarrow{AC}$
b) $\overrightarrow{AQ}$ **d)** $\overrightarrow{BC}$ **f)** $\overrightarrow{BD}$

Q4   In the diagram on the right, EB and AC are perpendicular. ABCE is a parallelogram. $\angle$EDC is a right angle.

a) Name a vector equal to:

    i) $\overrightarrow{FC}$ **iii)** $\overrightarrow{BC}$ **v)** $2\overrightarrow{CD}$ **vii)** $\overrightarrow{EF} - \overrightarrow{CF}$
    ii) $\overrightarrow{FB}$ **iv)** $\overrightarrow{CE}$ **vi)** $\overrightarrow{AE} + \overrightarrow{EC}$ **viii)** $\overrightarrow{ED} + \overrightarrow{DC} + \overrightarrow{CB}$

b) If AC = 16 cm and EB = 6 cm:
    i) what is the area of ABCE?   **ii)** what is the area of ABCDE?

c) Find:
    i) $|\overrightarrow{AE}|$ **ii)** $|\overrightarrow{CD}|$ **iii)** $|\overrightarrow{CF}|$ **iv)** $|\overrightarrow{AD}|$ **v)** $|\overrightarrow{FD}|$ **vi)** $|\overrightarrow{BD}|$

Vectors

Look at the pretty pictures... make sure you can see how this little lot fit with the questions.

Q5 In still water my motor boat can achieve 9 km/h. I aim the boat directly across the river which is running at 3 km/h. What is my resultant speed?

Q6

Casey is taking part in a swimming race across a river. The river flows at 2 km/h. Casey can swim at 3.5 km/h.

a) What angle to the bank should she swim to go directly across the river and have the best chance of winning?

b) Calculate her resultant speed.

Q7 An aircraft is attempting to fly due north. The plane travels at 600 km/h, but the pilot has to compensate for a strong 75 km/h wind from the west, as shown.

a) What bearing should the pilot fly the plane on to avoid being blown off course?

b) Calculate the aircraft's resultant speed.

Remember — bearings are measured clockwise from the north line.

Q8 Point A has position vector $\mathbf{a} = \begin{pmatrix} 2 \\ 3 \end{pmatrix}$ and point B has position vector $\mathbf{b} = \begin{pmatrix} -1 \\ 5 \end{pmatrix}$

a) Find the position vectors of:
  i) point C when $\mathbf{c} = \mathbf{b} + 3\mathbf{a}$
  ii) point D when $\mathbf{d} = \mathbf{a}^2 - \mathbf{b}$

b) Find:
  i) $|\overrightarrow{AB}|$ **iii)** $|\overrightarrow{BD}|$
  ii) $|\overrightarrow{CD}|$ **iv)** $|\overrightarrow{CA}|$

Q9 In the following diagrams, forces are acting on an object as shown.

For each find:
a) the resultant force
b) its direction in relation to the larger force.

Put the vectors end to end and complete the triangle.

Matrices

The key to doing calculations with matrices is remembering to do things in the right order. I recommend starting with question 1...

Q1 Calculate:

a) $\begin{pmatrix} 5 & 2 \\ 8 & 1 \end{pmatrix} + \begin{pmatrix} 4 & 7 \\ 3 & 6 \end{pmatrix}$

d) $\begin{pmatrix} -2 & -5 \\ 9 & 4 \end{pmatrix} + \begin{pmatrix} -7 & 5 \\ 3 & 6 \end{pmatrix}$

g) $\begin{pmatrix} 2 & 8 & 1 \\ 4 & 3 & -5 \end{pmatrix} + \begin{pmatrix} 7 & -9 & -2 \\ 5 & 10 & 6 \end{pmatrix}$

b) $\begin{pmatrix} 11 & 3 \\ 2 & 9 \end{pmatrix} - \begin{pmatrix} 8 & 1 \\ 6 & 3 \end{pmatrix}$

e) $\begin{pmatrix} -3 & 12 \\ 8 & -1 \end{pmatrix} - \begin{pmatrix} 1 & 2 \\ -7 & -6 \end{pmatrix}$

h) $\begin{pmatrix} 5 & 12 & -8 \\ -10 & 2 & 7 \end{pmatrix} - \begin{pmatrix} 3 & 4 & 6 \\ -5 & -9 & 9 \end{pmatrix}$

c) $\begin{pmatrix} 3 & 21 \\ 8 & 5 \end{pmatrix} + \begin{pmatrix} 1 & 2 \\ 10 & 9 \end{pmatrix}$

f) $\begin{pmatrix} 17 & 10 \\ 20 & -15 \end{pmatrix} - \begin{pmatrix} -14 & -21 \\ 30 & 23 \end{pmatrix}$

i) $\begin{pmatrix} 8 & -8 \\ 3 & 5 \\ 11 & 4 \end{pmatrix} - \begin{pmatrix} 1 & 1 \\ -3 & 7 \\ 9 & 2 \end{pmatrix}$

Q2 A matrix, <u>A</u>, has 2 rows and 2 columns.
A second matrix, <u>B</u>, has 3 columns and 2 rows.
a) Can you add <u>A</u> + <u>B</u>?
b) Can you multiply <u>A</u> × <u>B</u>?
c) Can you multiply <u>B</u> × <u>A</u>?
A third matrix, <u>C</u>, has 2 rows and 2 columns.
d) Can you subtract <u>A</u> – <u>C</u>?
e) Can you multiply <u>C</u> × <u>A</u>?

Q3 Evaluate:

a) $3\begin{pmatrix} 2 & 5 \\ 1 & 7 \end{pmatrix}$

c) $-1\begin{pmatrix} 8 & 3 \\ 13 & -5 \end{pmatrix}$

e) $4\begin{pmatrix} 2 & 8 & -1 \\ 9 & 6 & -3 \end{pmatrix}$

g) $2\begin{pmatrix} 9 & -5 \\ -2 & -3 \\ 7 & -1 \end{pmatrix}$

b) $8\begin{pmatrix} 4 & 10 \\ 5 & 6 \end{pmatrix}$

d) $-5\begin{pmatrix} -2 & 5 \\ 11 & 3 \end{pmatrix}$

f) $-3\begin{pmatrix} 7 & 1 & 3 \\ -2 & 4 & -1 \end{pmatrix}$

h) $-8\begin{pmatrix} 3 & -4 & 5 \\ 9 & -2 & 1 \end{pmatrix}$

Q4 Find:

a) $\begin{pmatrix} 4 & 3 \\ 7 & 2 \end{pmatrix}\begin{pmatrix} 1 & 5 \\ 3 & 9 \end{pmatrix}$

d) $\begin{pmatrix} 2 \\ 6 \\ -3 \end{pmatrix}(1 \ 5 \ 4)$

g) $\begin{pmatrix} -3 \\ -1 \end{pmatrix}(5 \ 2 \ 4 \ 8 \ -1)$

b) $\begin{pmatrix} 7 & -1 \\ 12 & 2 \end{pmatrix}\begin{pmatrix} 3 & -2 \\ 2 & 5 \end{pmatrix}$

e) $\begin{pmatrix} 1 & 7 \\ -4 & 3 \end{pmatrix}\begin{pmatrix} 5 & -2 & -1 \\ 8 & 5 & 5 \end{pmatrix}$

h) $(-5 \ 1)\begin{pmatrix} 4 & -3 & -2 \\ 8 & 4 & 1 \end{pmatrix}$

c) $\begin{pmatrix} 5 & 10 \\ 2 & 4 \end{pmatrix}\begin{pmatrix} 7 & 3 \\ 11 & -20 \end{pmatrix}$

f) $\begin{pmatrix} 5 & 2 & -2 \\ 8 & 4 & 1 \end{pmatrix}\begin{pmatrix} 7 \\ 5 \\ -3 \end{pmatrix}$

i) $\begin{pmatrix} 2 & -3 & 1 \\ 11 & -1 & -5 \end{pmatrix}\begin{pmatrix} 10 & 2 \\ 12 & 7 \\ 5 & 4 \end{pmatrix}$

Matrices

Q5 Solve:

a) $\begin{pmatrix} -1 & 5 \\ 3 & 9 \end{pmatrix} + \begin{pmatrix} 2 & 2 \\ -4 & 8 \end{pmatrix}$

c) $-5\begin{pmatrix} 4 & 8 \\ 3 & -4 \end{pmatrix}$

e) $\begin{pmatrix} -1 & 7 \\ -4 & 3 \end{pmatrix}\begin{pmatrix} 5 & -8 \\ 3 & 2 \end{pmatrix}$

g) $-3\begin{pmatrix} 4 & 5 & -1 \\ 8 & 2 & 10 \end{pmatrix}$

b) $\begin{pmatrix} 13 & -5 \\ -1 & 2 \end{pmatrix} - \begin{pmatrix} 8 & -3 \\ 6 & 2 \end{pmatrix}$

d) $11\begin{pmatrix} 2 & 5 \\ 11 & -1 \end{pmatrix}$

f) $\begin{pmatrix} 10 & 0 \\ -9 & 1 \end{pmatrix}\begin{pmatrix} 5 & 6 \\ -12 & 3 \end{pmatrix}$

h) $5\begin{pmatrix} 5 & 9 \\ 5 & 3 \end{pmatrix} - 2\begin{pmatrix} 13 & 6 \\ -4 & 1 \end{pmatrix}$

Q6 Write the result of the following matrix calculations:

a) $\begin{pmatrix} 2 & 10 \\ 7 & -9 \end{pmatrix}\begin{pmatrix} 0 & 0 \\ 0 & 0 \end{pmatrix}$

b) $\begin{pmatrix} 4 & -15 \\ 7 & 100 \end{pmatrix} + \begin{pmatrix} 0 & 0 \\ 0 & 0 \end{pmatrix}$

c) $\begin{pmatrix} 8 & 12 \\ 2 & 3 \end{pmatrix}\begin{pmatrix} 1 & 0 \\ 0 & 1 \end{pmatrix}$

d) $\begin{pmatrix} 1 & 0 \\ 0 & 1 \end{pmatrix}\begin{pmatrix} 91 & -50 \\ -1 & 2 \end{pmatrix}$

Q7 Show that $\begin{pmatrix} 3 & 7 \\ 6 & 14 \end{pmatrix}$ is singular.

Q8 For each of these matrices, find the inverse or show that the inverse can't be found.

a) $\begin{pmatrix} 8 & 1 \\ 4 & 3 \end{pmatrix}$

c) $\begin{pmatrix} 4 & 7 \\ 5 & -2 \end{pmatrix}$

e) $\begin{pmatrix} 12 & 6 \\ -6 & -3 \end{pmatrix}$

g) $\begin{pmatrix} -10 & -5 \\ 6 & -3 \end{pmatrix}$

b) $\begin{pmatrix} 3 & 9 \\ 2 & 6 \end{pmatrix}$

d) $\begin{pmatrix} -2 & 8 \\ 1 & -4 \end{pmatrix}$

f) $\begin{pmatrix} -3 & 9 \\ -3 & 5 \end{pmatrix}$

h) $\begin{pmatrix} 12 & 5 \\ -9 & 11 \end{pmatrix}$

Q9 **a)** Etan says 'For any 2 × 2 matrix $\underline{A}$, you can find a matrix $\underline{B}$ so that $\underline{A} \times \underline{B} = \begin{pmatrix} 1 & 0 \\ 0 & 1 \end{pmatrix}$'. Is he right? Explain your answer.

b) Danni says 'For any 2 × 2 matrix $\underline{C}$, there's a matrix $\underline{D}$ where $\underline{C} \times \underline{D} = \begin{pmatrix} 0 & 0 \\ 0 & 0 \end{pmatrix}$'. Is she right? Explain your answer.

Q10 $\underline{A} = \begin{pmatrix} -2 & 8 \\ 3 & 4 \end{pmatrix}$ $\underline{B} = \begin{pmatrix} 11 & -1 \\ 12 & 1 \end{pmatrix}$ $\underline{C} = \begin{pmatrix} -3 & 10 \\ -7 & -5 \end{pmatrix}$ Find:

a) $\underline{A} + \underline{B}$

d) $2\underline{B}$

g) $2\underline{A} - 3\underline{C}$

j) $\begin{pmatrix} 0 & 0 \\ 0 & 0 \end{pmatrix} + \underline{B}$

b) $\underline{A} - \underline{B}$

e) $\underline{B} \times \underline{C}$

h) $\underline{B}^{-1}$

k) $\underline{C}\begin{pmatrix} 0 & 0 \\ 0 & 0 \end{pmatrix}$

c) $\underline{C} - \underline{A}$

f) $\underline{A} \times \underline{B}$

i) $\underline{C} \times \underline{C}^{-1}$

l) $\underline{A}\begin{pmatrix} 1 & 0 \\ 0 & 1 \end{pmatrix}$

Transformations

 Better to get these done quickly, or something might turn into a pumpkin... possibly. Best not to take the chance, anyhow.

Q1 A is the point (4, 3), B is (4, 1) and C is (5, 1).

a) Using a scale of 1 cm to 1 unit draw the axes and mark on it the figure given by ABC.

b) Reflect ABC in the *x*-axis and label the image $A_1B_1C_1$.

c) Reflect $A_1B_1C_1$ in the *y*-axis and label the image $A_2B_2C_2$.

d) Describe fully the single transformation which would map ABC onto $A_2B_2C_2$.

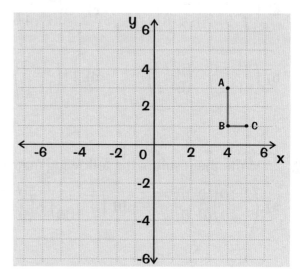

Q2 Copy the axes using a scale of 1 cm to 1 unit. Mark on the axes a quadrilateral Q with corners (-2, 1), (-3, 1), (-3, 3) and (-2, 2).

a) Rotate Q clockwise through 90° about the point (-1, 2). Label the image R.

b) Rotate R clockwise through 90° about the point (0, 1). Label the image S.

c) Describe fully the rotation that maps Q to S.

d) Rotate Q through 180° about the point (-½, -1). Label the image T.

e) Rotate Q anticlockwise through 90° about the point (-1, -1). Label the image U.

f) Describe fully the rotation that sends U to T.

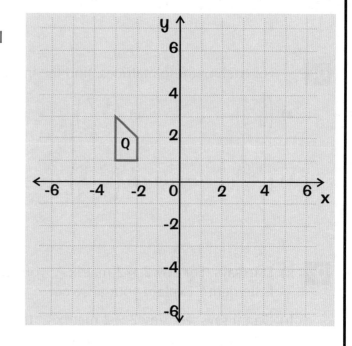

Q3 Draw axes with *x* and *y* running from 0 to 12 with a scale of 1 cm to 1 unit. O is the origin. $\overrightarrow{OP} = \binom{4}{2}$, $\overrightarrow{PQ} = \binom{-1}{2}$, and $\overrightarrow{QR} = 2\overrightarrow{OP}$.

a) Mark P, Q and R on your axes.

b) Translate R by $\overrightarrow{QO}$. Label the image T.

c) Verify that $\overrightarrow{PQ} + \overrightarrow{QR} + \overrightarrow{RT} + \overrightarrow{TP} = O$.

Urghh — <u>vectors</u>. <u>Make sure</u> you get the coordinates the right way round — <u>top</u> for the <u>x</u> direction, <u>bottom</u> for the <u>y</u> direction.

Transformations

Move each point separately — then check your shape hasn't done anything unexpected while you weren't looking.

Q4 Copy the axes and mark on triangle A with corners (-1, 2), (0, 4) and (-2, 4). Use a scale of 1 cm to 1 unit.

a) Reflect A in the line $y = -x$. Label this image B.

b) Reflect A in the line $x = 1$. Label the image C.

c) Reflect A in the line $y = -1$. Label the image D.

d) Translate triangle D with the vector $\binom{4}{2}$. Label this image E.

e) Translate triangle C with the vector $\binom{3}{-3}$. Label this image F.

f) Describe fully the rotation that sends C to E.

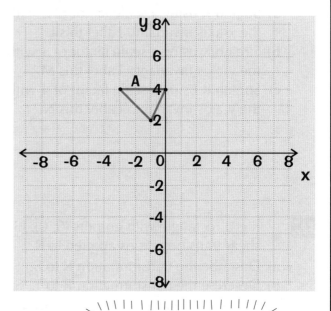

It helps to label the corners of the triangle so you can see exactly what goes where when you do the transformations.

Q5 Copy the axes below using a scale of 1 cm to 1 unit.

A parallelogram A has vertices at (6, 4), (10, 4), (8, 10) and (12, 10). Draw this parallelogram onto your axes.
An enlargement scale factor ½ and centre (0, 0) transforms parallelogram A onto its image B.

a) Draw parallelogram B on your axes.

b) Translate B by the vector $\binom{-3}{-2}$ and label this image C.

c) Calculate the ratio of the area of parallelogram C to the area of parallelogram A.

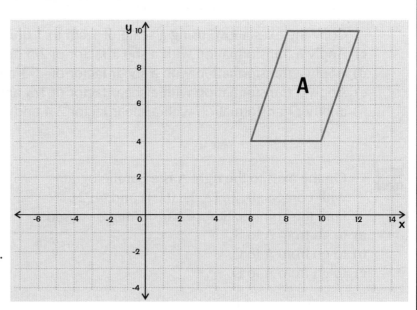

Transformations

Q6 Copy the axes shown on the right and mark on a kite, K, with corners (1, 2), (2, 1), (4, 2) and (2, 3).
Use a scale of 1 cm to 1 unit.

a) Stretch K using a scale factor of 2 with the x-axis invariant. Label this L.
b) Stretch K using a scale factor of 3 with the y-axis invariant. Label this M.
c) Stretch K using a scale factor of 4 with the y-axis invariant. Label this N.

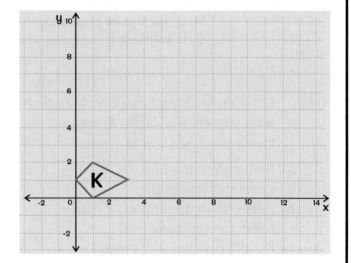

Q7 R is a rectangle with corners (0, 0), (3, 0), (3, 5) and (0, 5). S and T are the results of shear transformations applied to R.

a) Describe the transformation R to S. Specify the invariant line and the shear factor.
b) Describe the transformation R to T. Specify the invariant line and the shear factor.

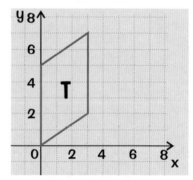

Copy the axes above using a scale of 1 cm to 1 unit. Mark on the rectangle R.
c) Apply a transformation with a shear factor of 2/5 and the x-axis invariant. Label this U.
d) Apply a transformation with a shear factor of -1/3 and the y-axis invariant. Label this V.
e) Apply a transformation with a shear factor of 1/5 and the x-axis invariant. Then apply another transformation with a shear factor 2/4 and the y-axis invariant. Label this W.

Q8 On the axes to the right A is a parallelogram with corners (0, 2), (2, 1), (6, 1) and (4, 2).
Find the combination of transformations used:
a) to go from A to B
b) to go from A to C
c) to go from A to D

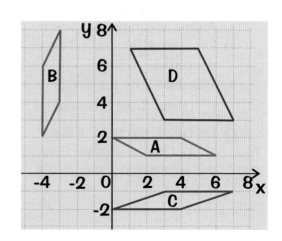

Transformations

Q9 Draw a set axes with scales ranging from –8 to 8 in both directions.
Use the axes to draw the shapes represented by the following matrices:

a) $\underline{A} = \begin{pmatrix} 0 & 4 & 2 \\ 1 & 1 & 3 \end{pmatrix}$

c) $\underline{C} = \begin{pmatrix} -2 & -3 & -5 & -6 \\ -3 & -5 & -3 & -5 \end{pmatrix}$

e) $\underline{E} = \begin{pmatrix} 1 & 2 & 3 & 4 & 3 & 2 \\ -6 & -5 & -6 & -6 & -7 & -6 \end{pmatrix}$

b) $\underline{B} = \begin{pmatrix} 3 & 7 & 7 & 3 \\ 6 & 6 & 7 & 7 \end{pmatrix}$

d) $\underline{D} = \begin{pmatrix} 4 & 5 & 6 & 5 & 4 & 3 \\ -2 & -2 & -3 & -4 & -4 & -3 \end{pmatrix}$

f) $\underline{F} = \begin{pmatrix} -2 & -4 & -5 & -6 & -8 & -6 & -5 & -4 \\ 4 & 3 & 1 & 3 & 4 & 5 & 7 & 5 \end{pmatrix}$

Q10 Draw axes for $x = -8$ to 8 and $y = -8$ to 8 with a scale of 1 cm to 1 unit

a) Draw the shape A represented by $\underline{A} = \begin{pmatrix} 1 & 6 & 6 & 1 \\ 1 & 1 & 3 & 3 \end{pmatrix}$.

Apply the following transformations and draw the resulting shapes B, C, D and E:

b) $\underline{TA} = \underline{B}$ where $\underline{T} = \begin{pmatrix} 0 & -1 \\ 1 & 0 \end{pmatrix}$

d) $\underline{TA} = \underline{D}$ where $\underline{T} = \begin{pmatrix} -1 & 0 \\ 0 & 1 \end{pmatrix}$

c) $\underline{TA} = \underline{C}$ where $\underline{T} = \begin{pmatrix} 1 & 0 \\ 0 & -1 \end{pmatrix}$

e) $\underline{TA} = \underline{E}$ where $\underline{T} = \begin{pmatrix} 0 & 1 \\ -1 & 0 \end{pmatrix}$

Q11 Write down the matrices which describe
the shapes shown on the axes to the right:

a) R   **c)** S   **e)** T
b) R'   **d)** S'   **f)** T'

Find the matrices for the transformations:

g) R ⟶ R'
h) S ⟶ S'
i) T ⟶ T'

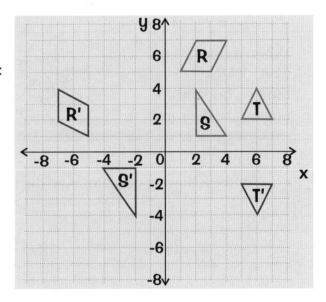

Q12 Find the matrices resulting from the following transformations:

a) Rectangle $\underline{A} = \begin{pmatrix} 4 & 7 & 7 & 4 \\ 2 & 2 & 7 & 7 \end{pmatrix}$ is transformed by $\underline{G} = \begin{pmatrix} 0 & -1 \\ 1 & 0 \end{pmatrix}$ and then by $\underline{H} = \begin{pmatrix} 0 & 2 \\ -1 & 0 \end{pmatrix}$ to give $\underline{D}$.

b) Triangle $\underline{B} = \begin{pmatrix} 1 & 5 & 1 \\ -4 & -6 & -6 \end{pmatrix}$ is transformed by $\underline{M} = \begin{pmatrix} 1 & 0 \\ 0 & -1 \end{pmatrix}$ and then by $\underline{N} = \begin{pmatrix} 2 & 1 \\ 1 & -1 \end{pmatrix}$ to give $\underline{E}$.

c) Parallelogram $\underline{C} = \begin{pmatrix} -2 & -2 & -5 & -5 \\ 4 & 5 & 4 & 3 \end{pmatrix}$ is transformed by $\underline{R} = \begin{pmatrix} -2 & 0 \\ 0 & 3 \end{pmatrix}$

and then by $\underline{S} = \begin{pmatrix} 5 & -3 \\ 0 & -1 \end{pmatrix}$ to give $\underline{F}$.

When combining matrix transformations
remember to multiply them in reverse order
...second, first, original.

Geometry

Here are some angle rules then — just the 7 for now. You can't get away without knowing these, I'm afraid, so get learning.

1) Angles in a triangle <u>add up to 180°</u>

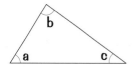

2) Angles in a 4-sided shape <u>add up to 360°</u>

3) Angles round a point <u>add up to 360°</u>

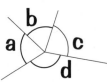

4) When a line crosses <u>TWO PARALLEL LINES</u>, the two bunches of angles are the same

5) Angles on a straight line <u>add up to 180°</u>

6) <u>ISOSCELES TRIANGLES</u> have two sides the same and two angles the same

7) <u>EXTERIOR</u> angle of a triangle = sum of opposite <u>INTERIOR</u> angles.

d = a + b

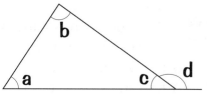

For the following diagrams, find the <u>lettered</u> angles. LM is a straight line.

Q1 a) b) c) d)

Q2 a)

b)

c)

d)

Geometry

This page is a bit dull — just lots of boring angles... still, that's geometry for you. Oh and by the way, you've got to work the angles out — don't try and sneakily measure them, they're probably drawn wrong anyway...

For the following diagrams, find the <u>lettered</u> angles.   LM is a straight line.

Q3 a)

b)

c)

d)

Q4 a)

b)

c)

\\\\\ \ \\\\\\\\\\\\\\\\\\\\\\\\/ / / / / /,
Keep an eye out for parallel lines — they'll help no end...
as long as you can remember the angle rules, of course.
/ \ \ \ \ \

Q5 a)

b)

c)

Q6 a)

b)

c)

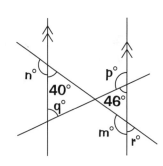

Circle Geometry

Q1 Using π = 3.14, find:
  a) The area of a circle with radius = 6.12 m. Give your answer <u>to 3 dp</u>.
  b) The circumference of a circle with radius = 7.2 m. Give your answer <u>to 2 sf</u>.
  c) The circumference of a circle with diameter = 14.8 m. Give your answer <u>to 1 dp</u>.
  d) The area of a circle with diameter = 4.246 cm. Give your answer <u>to 3 dp</u>.

Q2 Find the <u>area and the perimeter</u> of each of the shapes drawn here. Use π = 3.14.

a)

b)

c)

Q3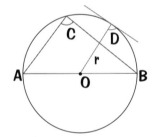

The circle in the diagram to the left contains a triangle with points (A and B) at both ends of a diameter and angle C to the edge of the circle. A tangent has been drawn which makes angle D with the radius, r. O is the centre of the circle.
What are the sizes of the angles C and D?

Q4 A tangent of a circle is drawn, touching it at A.
C and B are two other points on the circumference and AOB is a diameter. O is the centre of the circle. Angle ABC is 23°.
  a) Write down the size of angle ACB, giving a reason for your answer.
  b) Find the size of the angle marked x° in the diagram.

Q5

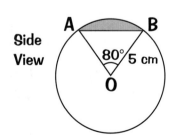

Side View

A washing powder ball looks from the side like a circle with the shaded area removed. The circle has radius 5 cm and the angle AOB = 80°.
  a) Find the area of the sector OAB.
  b) Find the area of triangle AOB and hence the area of the shaded area.

The formula you need for part b) is area = ½absin(c).

Circle Geometry

Q6   ABCD is a cyclic quadrilateral with angle BCD = 100°.
EF is a tangent to the circle touching it at A.
Angle DAF = 30°.
Write down the size of angle:
a) BAD
b) EAB.

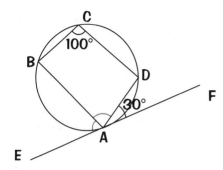

Q7   A, B, and C are points on the circumference of a circle with
centre O. BD and CD are tangents of the circle.
a) State the length BD.
b) Calculate the angle COD.
c) State the angle COB.
d) Find the angle CAB.

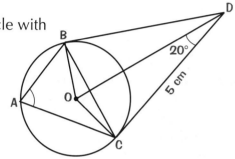

Q8   A, B, C, D and E are points on the circumference of
a circle with centre O. Angle BDE = 53°. The line
AF is a tangent to the circle, touching it at A.
Angle EAF = 32°. Find:
a) angle BOE
b) angle ACE.

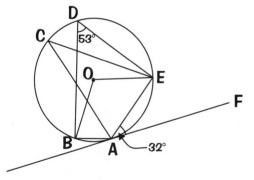

Q9   ABCD is a cyclic quadrilateral and the tangent
to the circle at A makes an angle of 70° with
the side AD. O is the centre of the circle.
Write down, giving a reason, the size of:
a) angle ACD
b) angle BAD.

Q10

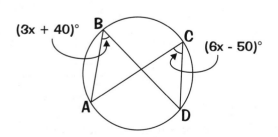

A, B, C and D are points on the
circumference of a circle.
Angle ABD = $(3x + 40)$° and
angle ACD = $(6x – 50)$°.
a) Give a reason why angle ABD and
angle ACD must be the same size.
b) Form an equation in x and solve it
to find the size of angle ABD.

Circle Geometry

Q11   O is the centre of a circle and AB is a chord.
The length OA = 5 cm and angle OAB = 20°.
Find the length of the chord AB.

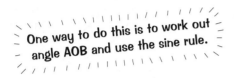

One way to do this is to work out angle AOB and use the sine rule.

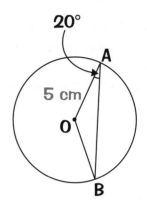

Q12   A, B, C and D are points on the circumference
of a circle. O is the centre of the circle and
angle AOD = 140°. Write down:
a) angle ABD
b) angle ABC
c) angle DBC.

Q13

ABCD is a cyclic quadrilateral. The lines AC and
BD intersect at X. AX = 4 cm, DX = 8 cm and
XC = 10 cm. Angles DXC = 85° and ABD = 30°.
a) Show that triangles DXC and AXB are similar.
b) Find the length of XB.
c) Write down the size of angle BDC.

Q14   B, C and D are three points on the circumference of
a circle with BD as a diameter. O is the centre of the
circle and ADC is a straight line.
AB = 10 cm and BC = 3 cm.
a) Write down the size of angle ACB, giving a
reason for your answer.
b) Show that AC is 9.54 cm correct to 2 decimal places.
c) If AD = 5 cm, find the length of the diameter DOB correct to 2 decimal places.

Pythagoras' Theorem and Bearings

Don't try and do it all in your head — you've got to label the sides or you're bound to mess it up. Go on, get your pen out...

Q1 Find the length of the hypotenuse in each of the following triangles.

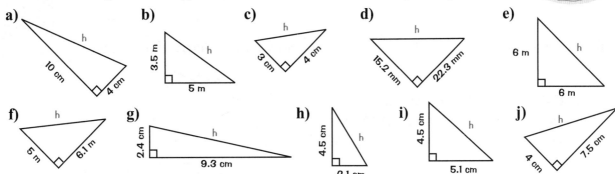

a) 10 cm, 4 cm, h

b) 3.5 m, 5 m, h

c) 3 cm, 4 cm, h

d) 15.2 mm, 22.3 mm, h

e) 6 m, 6 m, h

f) 5 m, 6.1 m, h

g) 2.4 cm, 9.3 cm, h

h) 4.5 cm, 2.1 cm, h

i) 4.5 cm, 5.1 cm, h

j) 4 cm, 7.5 cm, h

Q2 Find the length of the shorter side in each of the following triangles.

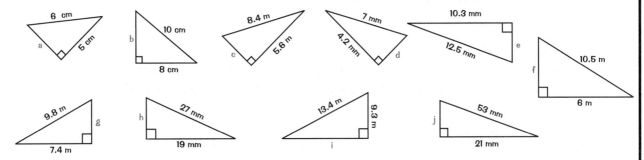

6 cm, 5 cm, a
b, 10 cm, 8 cm
8.4 m, 5.6 m, c
7 mm, 4.2 mm, d
10.3 mm, 12.5 mm, e
10.5 m, 6 m, f
9.8 m, 7.4 m, g
h, 27 mm, 19 mm
13.4 m, 9.3 m, i
53 mm, 21 mm, j

Q3 Find the unknown length in each of the following triangles.

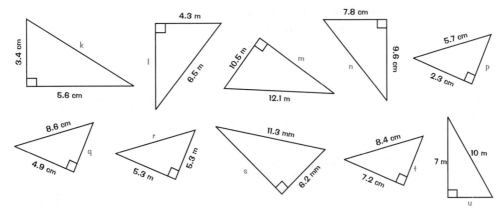

3.4 cm, 5.6 cm, k
4.3 m, 6.5 m, l
10.5 m, 12.1 m, m
7.8 cm, 9.6 cm, n
5.7 cm, 2.3 cm, p
8.6 cm, 4.9 cm, q
r, 5.3 m, 5.3 m
11.3 mm, 6.2 mm, s
8.4 cm, 7.2 cm, t
7 m, 10 m, u

Q4 Calculate the bearings required in these diagrams.

It's easy to get lost if you don't follow the rule: always measure bearings from the <u>north line</u>.

a) N, B, 65°, A, B to A

b) N, 130°, B, C to B, C

c) N, C, D to C, 215°, D

d) E, 49°, N, D, E to D

e) N, 117°, F, G, F to E, F to G, G to F

f) N, H, 76°, I, 145°, J, I to J, I to H, H to I

Pythagoras' Theorem and Bearings

Q5 A window cleaner wants to clean the upstairs windows of an office. To meet safety regulations, his 10 m long ladder needs to be angled so that the bottom of the ladder is at least 2.6 m away from the wall. What is the maximum height that the top of the ladder can reach when used safely? Give your answer to 1 decimal place.

Q6 A rectangular field is 250 m by 190 m. How far is it across diagonally?

Q7 **a)** Calculate the lengths WY and ZY.
b) What is the total distance WXYZW?
c) What is the area of quadrilateral WXYZ?

Q8 A plane flies due east for 153 km then turns and flies due north for 116 km. How far is it now from where it started?

Q9 A coastguard spots a boat on a bearing of 040° and at a distance of 350 m. He can also see a tree due east of him. The tree is due south of the boat.
a) Draw a scale diagram and measure accurately the distances from the:
i) boat to the tree
ii) coastguard to the tree
b) Check by Pythagoras to see if your answers are reasonable.

The word "<u>from</u>" is the most important word in a bearings question, so look out for it — it tells you where to start <u>from</u>.

Q10 Four towns W, X, Y and Z are situated as follows:
W is 90 km north of X, Y is on a bearing 175° and 165 km from X, X is on a bearing 129° and 123 km from Z. Draw an accurate scale diagram to represent the situation.
From your drawing measure the distances:
a) WZ   **b)** WY   **c)** ZY.
Measure the bearings:
d) Y from Z   **e)** W from Z   **f)** Y from W.

Q11 A walker travels 1200 m on a bearing of 165° and then another 1500 m on a bearing of 210°. By accurate measurement, find how far she is now from her starting point. What bearing must she walk on to return to base?

Q12 A fishing boat travels at 12 km/h for an hour due north. It then turns due west and travels at 7 km/h for an hour. How far is it from its starting point now? What bearing must it travel on to return to base?

Trigonometry

Before you start a trigonometry question, write down the ratios, using
SOH CAH TOA (<u>Sockatoa</u>!) — it'll help you pick your formula.

Q1   Calculate the tan, sin and cos of each of these angles:
     a) 17°   **b)** 83°   **c)** 5°   **d)** 28°   **e)** 45°.

Q2   Use the tangent ratio to find the unknowns:

Q3   Use the cosine ratio to find the unknowns:

Q4   Use the sine ratio to find the unknowns:

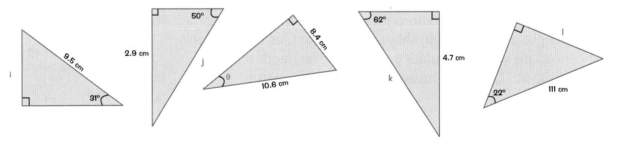

Q5   Find the unknowns using the appropriate ratios:

SECTION SIX — ANGLES AND GEOMETRY

Trigonometry

Q6 A right-angled triangle has sides measuring 30 m, 40 m and 50 m.
    a) Draw a rough sketch of the triangle, clearly labelling the hypotenuse.
    b) Calculate the size of the smallest angle.

> Make sure you've got the hang of the inverse SIN, COS and TAN functions on your calc... and check it's in DEG mode or you'll get nowhere fast.

Q7 The points P(1, 2), Q(4, 2) and R(4, -3) when joined together form a right-angled triangle.
    a) Draw a rough sketch of the triangle, labelling the length of each side.
    b) <u>Without measuring</u>, calculate the angle RPQ.
    c) <u>Deduce</u> angle PRQ.

Q8 The points A(1, -2), B(4, -1) and C(1, 3) are the vertices of the triangle ABC.
    a) On graph paper, <u>plot</u> the points A, B and C.
    b) By adding a suitable horizontal line, or otherwise, calculate the angle CAB.
    c) Similarly calculate the angle ACB.
    d) By using the fact that the interior angles of a triangle add up to 180° work out the angle ABC.

Q9 Mary was lying on the floor looking up at the star on top of her Christmas tree. She looked up through an angle of 55° when she was 1.5 m from the base of the tree. How high was the star?

Q10 Geoff is tiling his bathroom. He needs to cut off the right-angled triangle shown so that the tiles will fit nicely on his wall. Calculate the angle, θ, he needs to cut the tile at. Give your answer to the nearest degree.

Q11 Mr Brown took his dog for a walk in the park. The dog's lead was 2 m long. The dog ran 0.7 m from the path Mr Brown was walking on.

What angle did the lead make with the path?

Q12 A boat travels 9 km due south and then 7 km due east. What bearing must it travel on to return to base?

Trigonometry

Q13 This isosceles triangle has a base of 28 cm and a top angle of 54°. Calculate:

a) the length of sides AC and BC
b) the perpendicular height to C
c) the area of the triangle.

Q14 An isosceles triangle has two equal sides of 7 cm and an angle between them of 65°. Calculate the area of the triangle.

Q15 In this parallelogram the diagonal CB is at right angles to AC. AB is 9.5 cm and ∠CAB is 60°. Calculate:

a) CB   b) BD   c) the area of the parallelogram.

Q16 This rhombus WXYZ has base 15 cm and diagonal WY of 28 cm. Calculate the:

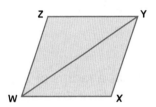

a) length of diagonal XZ
b) area of the rhombus
c) angle WY makes with WX.

Q17 Two mountains are 1020 m and 1235 m high. Standing on the summit of the lower one I look up through an angle of elevation of 16° to see the summit of the higher one. Calculate the horizontal distance between the two mountains.

Q18 A girl is flying a kite. She holds the string, which is 45 m long, at a height of 1.3 m above the ground. The string of the kite makes an angle of 33° with the horizontal. What is the vertical height of the kite from the ground?

Q19 I am standing on top of an 80 m high tower. I look due north and see two cars with angles of depression of 38° and 49°. Calculate:
a) how far each car is from the base of the tower
b) how far apart the cars are.

Q20 A ship sails on a bearing of 300° for 100 km. The captain can then see a lighthouse due south of him that he knows is due west of his starting point. Calculate how far west the lighthouse is from the ship's starting point.

114

3D Pythagoras and Trigonometry

Q1

This rectangular box is 20 cm by 12 cm by 9 cm.
Calculate:
a) angle ABE
b) length AF
c) length DF
d) angle EBH.

Q2 This pyramid is on a square base of side 56 cm.
Its vertical height is 32 cm. Calculate the length of:
a) the line from E to the mid-point of BC
b) the sloping edge BE.

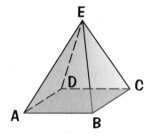

Q3 A rectangular box measures 20 cm by 30 cm by 8 cm.
Calculate the lengths of:
a) the diagonal of each rectangular face
b) the diagonal through the centre of the box.

Q4 This glass has a radius of 2.8 cm. The straw in the glass
makes an angle of 70° with the base and protrudes 4 cm
above the rim.
a) How tall is the glass?
b) How long is the straw?

Q5 A shop sells the three different gift boxes
shown on the right. Katie wants to buy
the cheapest box that will fit a pen that is
10 cm long. Which box should she buy?

Q6 This cone has a perpendicular height of 9 cm.
The centre of the base is O. The slant line from X
makes an angle of 23° with the central axis. Calculate:
a) the radius of the base
b) the area of the base
c) the volume of the cone.

The Sine and Cosine Rules

Make sure you know the Sine Rule and <u>both forms</u> of the Cosine Rule.
The one to use depends on which angles and sides you're given.

Q1 Calculate the lengths required to 3 s.f.

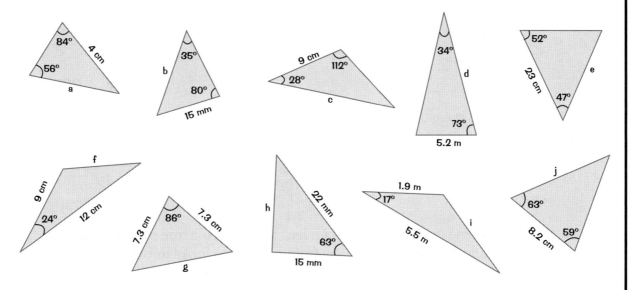

Q2 Calculate the angles required, to the nearest degree.

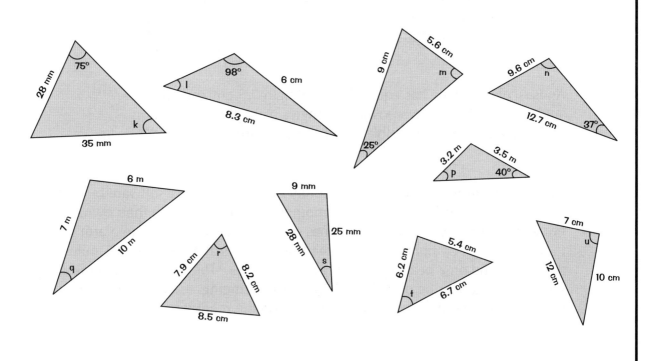

The Sine and Cosine Rules

Q3   Calculate the lettered sides and angles.

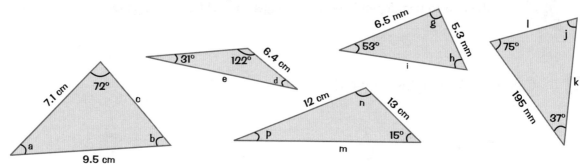

Q4   This field has measurements as shown. Calculate:
a) ∠ZXY
b) ∠XYZ
c) ∠YZX.

Q5   Peter is standing on a bridge over a river. He can see a tree on each bank, one 33 m and the other 35 m away from him. If he looks through an angle of 20° going from one tree to the other, how far apart are the two trees?

Q6   A coastguard sees a boat on a bearing of 038° from him and 25 km away. He also sees a ship 42 km away and on a bearing of 080°. Calculate:
a) the distance of the boat from the ship
b) the bearing of the boat from the ship.

Q7   An isosceles triangle has equal sides of length 7.5 cm and an angle of 56°. Sketch two possible triangles using this information and calculate the two possible lengths of the third side.

Q8   Air traffic control are testing the reliability of their computer software by monitoring two aeroplanes and checking the computer's calculations with their own. If the horizontal distance between the planes drops to 3 miles or less, an alarm should be triggered on the computer. One of the test planes is at a distance of 5 miles from the tower, and on a bearing of 020° from the tower. The second is at a distance of 4.6 miles on a bearing of 034° and the alarm is ringing. Calculate the horizontal distance between the planes and comment on the reliability of the software.

Q9   A parallelogram has sides of length 8 cm and 4.5 cm. One angle of the parallelogram is 124°. Calculate the lengths of the two diagonals.

The Sine and Cosine Rules

Q10 A vertical flagpole FP has two stay wires to the ground at A and B. They cannot be equidistant from P, as the ground is uneven. AB is 22 m, ∠PAB is 34° and ∠PBA is 50°. Calculate the distances:

a) PA

b) PB.

If A is level with P and the angle of elevation of F from A is 49°, calculate:

c) FA

d) PF.

Q11 An aircraft leaves A and flies 257 km to B on a bearing of 257°. It then flies on to C, 215 km away on a bearing of 163° from B. Calculate:

a) ∠ABC

b) distance CA

c) the bearing needed to fly from A direct to C.

Q12 On my clock the hour hand is 5.5 cm, the minute hand 8 cm and the second hand 7 cm, measured from the centre. Calculate the distance between the tips of the:

a) hour and minute hands at 10 o'clock

b) minute and second hands 15 seconds before 20 past the hour

c) hour and minute hands at 1020.

So the minute hand is at 19.75 minutes past the hour.

Q13 A surveyor wants to measure the height of a building. She measures the angle of elevation of the top of the building from the two different positions shown. Calculate the height of the building to the nearest metre.

Q14 Mary and Jane were standing one behind the other, 2.3 m apart, each holding one of the two strings of a kite flying directly in front of them. The angles of elevation of the kite from the girls were 65° and 48° respectively. Assuming the ends of both strings are held at the same height above the ground, calculate the length of each string.

Sine and Cosine for Larger Angles

Q1 Calculate the lettered sides and angles.

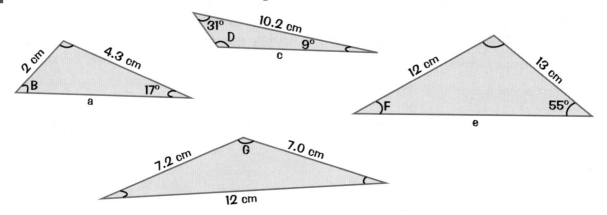

Q2 If $90° < x < 180°$, find x when:
a) $\sin x = 0.84$ b) $\sin x = 0.7$ c) $\sin x = 0.173$

Q3 Fayrmin looks upon a mystical glade. In the glade is a unicorn being guarded by 2 minotaurs. One minotaur is 23 metres from the unicorn, the other one is 14 metres from the unicorn. They stand either side of the unicorn at an angle of 118°. How far apart are the minotaurs?

Q4 Adam surveys a building from inside. He finds the angle between the floor and the front is 58° then he walks 120 m to the other end of the building where the roof meets the floor and finds the angle between them to be 13°. Calculate:
a) the angle between the front of the building and the roof
b) the length of: i) the building front   ii) the roof
c) the height of the highest point of the building.

Q5 A sailor sees a storm in the distance. The sailor knows that an island is 7 kilometres away from the boat and calculates that the angle between this island and the storm is 94° and that there is 26 kilometres of water between the storm and the island. Calculate the proximity of the ship to the storm.

Q6 PQR is a triangle. The size of angle P is 25°. Side r is 12 m long and side p is 7.5 m long. What are the two possible values of the size of angle R?

Q7 A spacecraft (S) is travelling to the moon. When it is 210 000 km from mission control on Earth (E) it is found to be 170 000 km away from the landing site at the moon base (M). The straight-line distance between mission control and the moon base is 370 000 km. Calculate the angle ESM. Give your answer to 1 d.p.

Mean, Median, Mode and Range

For finding the <u>mode</u> and <u>median</u> put the data in order of size — it's much easier to find the most frequent and middle values.

The <u>mean</u> involves a bit more calculation, but hey, you're doing maths...

Q1 The local rugby team scored the following number of tries in their first 10 matches of the season:

3	5	4	2	0	1	3	0	3	4

Find their modal number of tries.

Q2 Find the mean, median, mode and range of these numbers:

1	2	−2	0	1	8	3	−3	2	4	−2	2

Q3 A company has 9 employees in the sales department who earn commission. They are advertising for another salesperson and want to say in the advert how much commission their staff earn on average. The amount of commission the 9 existing salespeople earned last year is as follows:

£13,000	£9,000	£7,500
£18,000	£12,000	£7,500
£23,000	£15,000	£11,500

a) Find the mean, median and mode of their earnings.
b) Which one does not give a good indication of their average commission?
c) Which should the company put in the advert, and why?

Q4 Molly is writing a letter of complaint to the bus company because she thinks her bus to school is regularly late. Over 3 weeks, Molly kept a record of how many minutes her bus was either early or late, and put this in her letter. (She used + for late and – for early.)

+2	−1	0	+5	−4
−7	0	−8	0	+4
−4	−3	+14	+2	0

a) Calculate the mean lateness/earliness of the bus.
b) Calculate the median.
c) What is the mode?
d) The bus company use the answers to a), b) and c) to claim they are always on time. Is this true?

Q5 The average weight of the 11 players in a football team was 72.5 kg. The average weight of the 5 reserve players was 75.6 kg. What was the average weight of the whole squad? (Give your answer to 3 s.f.)

Be careful — you have to use the averages to find the total weight, then divide to find the new average.

Q6 The mean daily weight of potatoes sold in a greengrocer's from Monday to Friday was 14 kg. The mean daily weight of potatoes sold from Monday to Saturday was 15 kg. How many kg of potatoes were sold on Saturday?

Mean, Median, Mode and Range

Q7   Colin averaged 83% over 3 exams. His average for the first two exams was 76%.
What was Colin's score in the final exam?

Q8   The range for a certain list of numbers is 26, one of the numbers in the list is 48.
   a) What is the lowest possible value a number in the list could be?
   b) What is the highest possible value that could be in the list?

Q9   An ordinary dice is rolled 6 times, landing on a different number each time.
   a) What is the mean score?
   b) What is the median score?
   c) What is the range of scores?

Q10   This bar graph shows the amount of time Jim and Bob spend
watching TV during the week.

   a) Find the mean amount of time per
   day each spends watching TV.

   b) Find the range of times for
   each of them.

   c) Using your answers from **a)** and **b)**,
   comment on what you notice about
   the way they watch TV.

Q11   Mr Jones posted 88 Christmas cards on Monday.
His friends received them over the week:
40 on Tuesday, 28 on Wednesday, 9 on Thursday,
6 on Friday and the remainder on Saturday.
   a) Find the modal number of days it took for the cards
   to arrive.
   b) Find the median number of days it took for the cards
   to arrive.
   c) "The majority of post arrives within 2 days."
   Is the above statement true or false in the
   light of the data?

Q12   In each of the following cases, decide which average is referred to:
   a) this average is least appropriate when the total number of values is small
   b) this average is most affected by the presence of extreme values.

Sampling Methods

Q1 Define:
a) random sampling
b) systematic sampling
c) stratified sampling

You've got to know the main types of sampling — make sure you can answer Q1 before going on to the rest.

Q2 Give a reason why the following methods of sampling are poor:
a) a survey carried out inside a newsagents concluded that 80% of the population buy a daily newspaper
b) a phone poll conducted at 11 am on a Sunday morning revealed that less than 2% of the population regularly go to church
c) 60% of the population were estimated to watch the 9 o'clock news each evening after a survey was carried out at a bridge club.

Q3 Decide which of the following questions (if any) are suitable for a survey to find which of five desserts (cheesecake, fruit salad, trifle, ice-cream sundae and chocolate cake) people like the most. Give a reason for each of your answers.
a) Do you like cheesecake, fruit salad, trifle, ice-cream sundae or chocolate cake?
b) How often do you eat dessert?
c) Which is your favourite out of: cheesecake; fruit salad; trifle; ice-cream sundae; chocolate cake?
d) What is your favourite dessert?
e) Is your favourite dessert: cheesecake; fruit salad; trifle; ice-cream sundae; chocolate cake; none of these?

Q4 A newspaper contained the following article regarding the amount of exercise teenagers take outside school.
a) Suggest 3 questions that you could use in a survey to find out whether this is true at your school.
b) At a particular school there are 300 pupils in each of years 7 to 11. There are approximately equal numbers of girls and boys.
Describe how you would select 10% of the pupils for a stratified sample which is representative of all the pupils at the school.

Over half of all teenagers do no exercise at all. Only one in ten play team sports or take part in individual sports. blah-blah-blah-blah-blah blah-blah-blah-blah-blah

Q5 Pauline is the manager of a small café. She knows that some of her customers buy cold drinks from the cold drinks machine, some buy hot drinks from the hot drinks machine and some people buy snacks and drinks at the counter.
Pauline would like to use a questionnaire to find out whether she should stock a new brand of cola. Here is part of Pauline's questionnaire:

Café Questionnaire
1) Please tick the box to show how often you visit the cafe:
daily ☐ weekly ☐ fortnightly ☐ monthly ☐ less than monthly ☐

a) Using the same style, design another question Pauline could use in her questionnaire.
b) Pauline hands out her questionnaire as she serves customers at the counter. Give a reason why this is a suitable or unsuitable way to hand out the questionnaire.

Frequency Tables

You've got to be able to do these in both row and
column form, because they could give you either one.
There's no real difference, and the rules are still the same.

Q1 To monitor their annual performance, a travel company logs all calls to their sales desk.
The number of calls per day received by the sales desk over a given year are shown here.

No. of Calls	10	11	12	13	14	15	16 and over
No. of Days	110	70	120	27	18	12	8

a) Find the median number of calls.
b) Find the modal number of calls.

Q2 A student has classes in Mathematics (M),
English (E), French (F), Art (A) and Science (S).
Her timetable is shown opposite.

Monday	S S E E A
Tuesday	E M M A A
Wednesday	S M E F F
Thursday	F E E A S
Friday	M M E S S

a) Complete the following frequency table for a week's lessons:

b) Calculate the number of French
lessons that the student will attend
during a 12-week term.

Subject	M	E	F	A	S
Frequency					

c) What is the modal lesson?

Q3 20 pupils are asked to estimate the length (to the nearest m) of their gardens.
Here are the results: 10, 8, 6, 4, 10, 8, 0, 14, 12, 8, 10, 6, 1, 6, 10, 8, 6, 6, 8, 8
Copy the frequency table below and put the estimates in.

a) Find the mode of the data.
b) Find the median of the data.
c) State the range of the data.

Length (m)	4 and under	6	8	10	12	14 and over
Frequency						

SECTION SEVEN — HANDLING DATA

Frequency Tables

Q4　130 female bus drivers were weighed to the nearest kg.
Complete the table and
use it to calculate:
a) the median weight
b) the modal weight
c) the mean weight

Weight (kg)	Frequency	Weight × Frequency
51	40	
52	30	
53	45	
54	10	
55	5	

Q5　A football magazine rates teams according to how many goals they're likely
to score in a match, based on their last 20 matches. The table below shows
the number of goals scored by Spark Bridge Wanderers over this period.

No. of goals	0	1	2	3	4	5	6
Frequency	0	1	1	7	6	3	2

Find the mean, mode and median of the data.

Q6　A tornado has struck the hamlet of Moose-on-the-Wold. Many houses have
had windows broken. The frequency table shows the devastating effects.

No. of windows broken per house	0	1	2	3	4	5	6
Frequency	5	3	4	11	13	7	2

a) Calculate the modal number of broken windows.
b) Calculate the median number of broken windows.
c) Calculate the mean number of broken windows.

Q7　Using the computerised till in a shoe shop, the manager can predict what stock to order
from the previous week's sales.
Opposite is the tabulated printout for
last week for men's shoes.

Shoe size	5	6	7	8	9	10	11
frequency	9	28	56	70	56	28	9

a) The mean, mode and median for this data can be compared. For each of the following
statements decide whether it is true or false.
　i)　The mode for this data is 70.
　ii)　The mean is greater than the median for this distribution.
　iii)　The mean, median and mode are all equal in this distribution.

b) What percentage of customers bought shoes of the mean size from last week's sales data:

　i) 30%　　ii) 70%　　iii) 0.273%　　or　　iv) 27.3%?

Grouped Frequency Tables

Q1 The speeds of 32 skiers at a certain corner of a downhill course are tabulated below.

Speed (km/h)	$40 \leq s < 45$	$45 \leq s < 50$	$50 \leq s < 55$	$55 \leq s < 60$	$60 \leq s < 65$
Frequency	4	8	10	7	3
Mid-Interval					
Frequency × Mid-Interval					

a) By completing the frequency table, estimate the mean speed.
b) How many skiers were travelling at less than 55 km/h?
c) How many skiers were travelling at 50 km/h or faster?

Q2 The weights in kg of 18 newly felled trees are noted below:
272.7 333.2 251.0 246.5 328.0 259.6 200.2 312.8 344.3
226.8 362.0 348.3 256.1 232.9 309.7 398.0 284.5 327.4

a) Complete the frequency table.

Weight (kg)	Tally	Frequency	Mid-Interval	Frequency × Mid-Interval
$200 \leq w < 250$				
$250 \leq w < 300$				
$300 \leq w < 350$				
$350 \leq w < 400$				

b) Estimate the mean weight using the frequency table.
c) What is the modal group?

Q3 48 numbers are recorded below:

0.057 0.805 0.056 0.979 0.419 0.160 0.534 0.763
0.642 0.569 0.773 0.055 0.349 0.892 0.664 0.136
0.528 0.792 0.085 0.546 0.549 0.908 0.639 0.000
0.614 0.478 0.421 0.472 0.292 0.579 0.542 0.356
0.070 0.890 0.883 0.333 0.033 0.323 0.544 0.668
0.094 0.049 0.049 0.999 0.632 0.700 0.983 0.356

a) Transfer the data into the frequency table.

Number	$0 \leq n < 0.2$	$0.2 \leq n < 0.4$	$0.4 \leq n < 0.6$	$0.6 \leq n < 0.8$	$0.8 \leq n < 1$
Tally					
Frequency					
Mid-Interval					
Frequency × Mid-Interval					

b) Write down the modal class(es).
c) Which group contains the median?
d) Estimate the mean value.

Histograms and Frequency Density

It's the <u>size that counts</u>... You've got to look at the <u>area</u> of the bars to find the frequency. That means looking at the <u>width</u> as well as the height.

Q1 The Bog Snorkelling Appreciation Society conducts a survey on the ages of all their members. The histogram below shows the age distribution of the people surveyed. The Society organises a 'Seniors' bog snorkelling event for members aged 60 or older. Use the graph to estimate the maximum number of people that might take part.

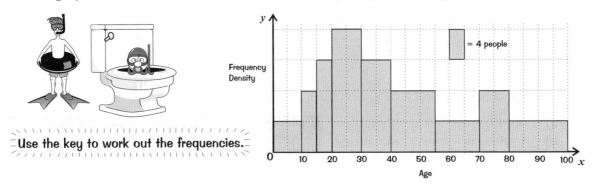

Use the key to work out the frequencies.

Q2 The weight of honey collected from several beehives is tabulated below.
a) Complete the frequency table by calculating the frequency densities.
b) Draw a histogram to represent this data.
c) Use your histogram to estimate the number of beehives that produced more than 6 kg of honey.

Weight (kg)	$0 \leq w < 2$	$2 \leq w < 4$	$4 \leq w < 7$	$7 \leq w < 9$	$9 \leq w < 15$
Frequency	3	2	6	9	12
Frequency density					

Q3 A local newspaper employee has collected data on the salaries of 100 people living in the area. His data is shown in the table below.

Salary (£1000s)	$0 \leq s < 10$	$10 \leq s < 20$	$20 \leq s < 30$	$30 \leq s < 40$	$40 \leq s < 50$
Frequency	10	25	42	20	3
Frequency Density					

a) Complete the table and draw a histogram to show the data.
b) The newspaper prints this histogram alongside the one shown on the right. It represents data from an identical survey done 10 years earlier. Write a comment comparing current salaries and those from 10 years ago.

Histograms and Frequency Density

Q4 A group of sixth formers took part in a survey to see how much time they spent watching TV each week.

a) Complete the table by filling in the frequency density column.
b) How many students took part in the survey?
c) Represent the data as a histogram.
d) Estimate the number of students that watch more than 7, but less than 13 hours each week.

No. of hours	Frequency	Frequency density
$0 \leq h < 1$	6	
$1 \leq h < 3$	13	
$3 \leq h < 5$	15	
$5 \leq h < 8$	9	
$8 \leq h < 10$	23	
$10 \leq h < 15$	25	
$15 \leq h < 20$	12	

Q5 A farmer keeps track of the amount of milk produced by his cows each day.

a) Complete the frequency table.
b) Use the mid-interval technique to estimate the mean.
c) Draw a histogram to show the data.
d) On how many days are less than 8 litres produced?

Amount of Milk (Litres)	Frequency	Frequency Density	Mid-Interval	Frequency × Mid-Interval
$0 \leq C < 1$	6			
$1 \leq C < 5$	6			
$5 \leq C < 8$	6			
$8 \leq C < 10$	6			
$10 \leq C < 15$	6			
$15 \leq C < 20$	6			

Q6 The publishers of a teen magazine want to increase its price.
To help them choose the best price, they carried out a survey of 188 readers to see how much pocket money they receive each week.

Amount (£)	Frequency	Frequency Density	Mid-Interval	Frequency × Mid-Interval
$0 \leq A < 0.50$	11			
$0.50 \leq A < 1.00$	25			
$1.00 \leq A < 1.30$	9			
$1.30 \leq A < 1.50$	12			
$1.50 \leq A < 1.80$	24			
$1.80 \leq A < 2.50$	21			
$2.50 \leq A < 3.10$	54			
$3.10 \leq A < 4.10$	32			

a) By first completing the table, estimate the mean amount of pocket money.
b) What is the modal class?

The publishers decide that £1.40 would be a reasonable price, but they want to check that at least 75% of readers could afford to buy the magazine with their pocket money.

c) Draw a histogram of the data and estimate how many readers receive less than £1.40.
d) Do 75% of readers receive £1.40 or more?

Cumulative Frequency

Q1 Using the cumulative frequency curve, read off the:
a) median
b) lower quartile
c) upper quartile
d) interquartile range.

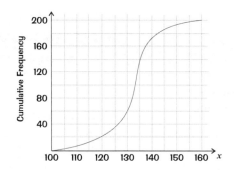

Q2 A daily survey is taken of the number of sheep in a field. The data is shown in this table:

No. Sheep	$0 \leq s < 5$	$5 \leq s < 10$	$10 \leq s < 15$	$15 \leq s < 20$	$20 \leq s < 25$	$25 \leq s < 30$
Frequency	3	9	14	7	4	2
Cumulative Frequency						

Complete the table then draw the cumulative frequency curve and use it to find the:
a) median   b) lower quartile   c) upper quartile   d) interquartile range
e) P_{90} to P_{10} percentile range   f) Comment on the difference between **d)** and **e)**

Q3 The number of passengers using a bus service each day has been recorded over a 4-week period. The data is presented in the table below:

No. passengers	$0 \leq n < 50$	$50 \leq n < 100$	$100 \leq n < 150$	$150 \leq n < 200$	$200 \leq n < 250$	$250 \leq n < 300$
Frequency	2	7	10	5	3	1
Cumulative Frequency						
Mid-Interval						
Frequency × Mid-Interval						

A mean passenger

a) By completing the table, estimate the mean number of passengers per day.
b) By plotting a cumulative frequency curve, determine the median value.
c) What is the modal group?

With cumulative frequency you always plot the highest value from each class.

Q4 40 pupils have taken an exam and their marks are recorded in a frequency table.

Mark (%)	$0 \leq m < 20$	$20 \leq m < 40$	$40 \leq m < 60$	$60 \leq m < 80$	$80 \leq m < 100$
Frequency	2	12	18	5	3
Cumulative Frequency					

a) Complete the table and plot the cumulative frequency curve.
b) What is the value of the lower quartile?
c) What is the interquartile range?
d) What is the median mark?

Cumulative Frequency

Q5 One hundred scores for a board game are presented in the table below.

Score	$31 \leq s < 41$	$41 \leq s < 51$	$51 \leq s < 61$	$61 \leq s < 71$	$71 \leq s < 81$	$81 \leq s < 91$	$91 \leq s < 101$
Frequency	4	12	21	32	19	8	4
Cumulative Frequency							

a) What is the modal group?
b) Which group contains the median score?
c) By plotting the cumulative frequency curve determine the actual value of the median score.
d) Find the interquartile range.

Q6 The following frequency table gives the distribution of the lives of electric bulbs.

a) Complete the frequency table.

Life (hours)	Frequency	Cumulative Frequency
$900 \leq L < 1000$	10	
$1000 \leq L < 1100$	12	
$1100 \leq L < 1200$	15	
$1200 \leq L < 1300$	18	
$1300 \leq L < 1400$	22	
$1400 \leq L < 1500$	17	
$1500 \leq L < 1600$	14	
$1600 \leq L < 1700$	9	

b) Which group contains the median value?
c) By drawing the cumulative frequency curve, find the actual value of the median.
d) Determine values for the upper and lower quartiles.

Q7 30 pupils recorded the time taken (minutes : seconds) to boil some water.
Here are their results:

2:37 2:37 3:17 3:30 2:45 2:13 3:18 3:12 3:38 3:29
3:04 3:24 4:13 3:01 3:11 2:33 3:37 4:24 3:59 3:11
3:22 3:13 2:57 3:12 3:07 4:17 3:31 3:42 3:51 3:24

a) By using a tally, transfer the data into the frequency table.
b) Draw the cumulative frequency curve.

Time	$2:00 \leq t < 2:30$	$2:30 \leq t < 3:00$	$3:00 \leq t < 3:30$	$3:30 \leq t < 4:00$	$4:00 \leq t < 4:30$
Tally					
Frequency					
Cumulative Frequency					

c) Using your graph, read off the median and the upper and lower quartiles.
d) What is the interquartile range?

Spread of Data

 Know your shapes — they're bound to ask you what different-shaped graphs mean, so get learning.

Q1 Match the histograms to their corresponding cumulative frequency curves.

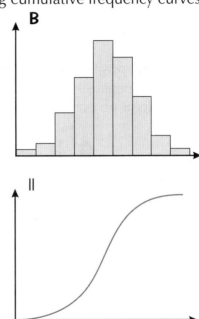

Q2 Below are two histograms — one shows the weights of a sample of 16 year olds, and the other shows the weights of a sample of 1 kg bags of sugar. Say which is which.

Q3 The charts below represent different data. Describe the spread of data in A and B.

a)

b)

c) One of the plots, A or B, represents the age of the population of the UK in 2010. Which one do you think it is? Explain why.

Scatter Graphs

A **SCATTER GRAPH** is just a load of points on a graph that <u>end up in a bit of a mess</u>, rather than in a nice line or curve. There's a fancy word to say how much of a mess they're in — it's <u>CORRELATION</u>.

Q1 Match the following diagrams with the most appropriate descriptive label.

Labels: (P) Strong positive correlation   (S) Moderate negative correlation
       (Q) Exact negative correlation   (T) Medium correlation
       (R) Little or no correlation   (U) Exact positive correlation.

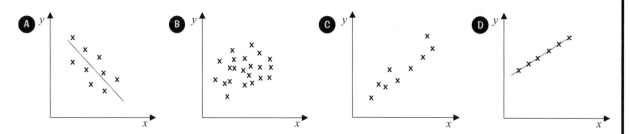

Q2 Adam thinks that cricketers who are good at batting must also be good at bowling. The bowling and batting averages for the members of his local team are given in the table.

Batting	8	13	17	26	29	35	37	40	45	52	57
Bowling	32	13	22	31	14	22	6	10	50	39	12

a) Draw a scatter diagram for the above data.
b) State the type of correlation, if any.
c) Is Adam correct in his assumption? Explain your answer.

> Good batters have a <u>high</u> batting average.
> Good bowlers have a <u>low</u> bowling average.

Q3 The examination results (%) for a class of students for 2 exams are shown in the table.

Physics	97	61	36	56	48	84	83	79	26	66
Chemistry	98	65	49	66	60	88	87	85	43	78

a) Represent the data with a scatter graph.
b) State the type of correlation, if any.
c) The students' science teacher thinks that the better a student is at physics, the better they'll be at chemistry. Do the exam results support this view?

Scatter Graphs

Q4 8 friends are comparing heights and shoe sizes to see if they are correlated.
The data is tabulated below:

Height	135 cm	140 cm	150 cm	155 cm	165 cm	180 cm	200 cm	215 cm
Shoe size	4	5	4.5	5	6	8	9	12

a) Plot the points on a scatter graph.
b) Are the points positively or negatively correlated?
c) Write a statement to explain the link between height and shoe size, from this data.
d) By fitting an appropriate line, estimate the shoe size of another friend who is 190 cm.

Q5 10 people took 2 exams in Welding for Beginners. The table shows the marks obtained.

Candidate	1	2	3	4	5	6	7	8	9	10
Exam 1 (%)	85	30	55	10	40	20	0	95	65	40
Exam 2 (%)	70	25	50	15	70	25	5	80	60	35

a) Draw a scatter graph representing this information.
b) Draw a line of best fit.
c) Clive only sat the first exam, obtaining a mark of 50%. Use your scatter graph to estimate the mark that he might have achieved if he had sat the second exam.

Q6 Janine is convinced that the more expensive cookery books contain more pages.
To test out her theory, she has compiled this table:

Price	£4.25	£5.00	£4.75	£6.25	£7.50	£8.25	£4.75	£5.00	£6.75	£3.25	£3.75
No. of pages	172	202	118	184	278	328	158	138	268	84	98

a) Draw a scatter graph to represent this information.
b) Draw in a line of best fit.
c) Use your line to estimate the price of a book containing 250 pages.

Q7 A local electrical store has kept a log of the number of CD players sold at each price:

Price (£)	£80	£150	£230	£310	£380	£460
No. Sold	27	24	22	19	17	15

a) Draw this information as a scatter graph, using suitable axes.
b) Draw a line of best fit and use it to estimate:
   i) the number of CD players the shopkeeper could expect to sell for £280
   ii) how much the shopkeeper should charge if he wanted to sell exactly 25 CD players.
c) Is the data positively or negatively correlated?

SECTION SEVEN — HANDLING DATA

Stem and Leaf Diagrams

The key to success with stem and leaf diagrams is, well, the key really.
Remember to include one if you're drawing your own diagram.

Q1 List the values shown in this stem and leaf diagram in ascending order.

Just to start you off, the first five values are:
3, 3, 3, 5, 8...

```
0 | 3 3 3 5 8 8 9
1 | 2 3 4 4 8 8 9
2 | 0 2 2 4
3 | 1 3
```

Key: 1 | 4   means 14

Q2 This stem and leaf diagram shows the marks in a test for a group of 25 students.

```
0  |
5  | 0 1
10 | 0 1 4
15 | 0 2 2 3 3 4
20 | 1 1 1 2 4 4
25 | 1 2 3 4
30 | 1 4 4
35 | 4
```

Key: 15 | 3   means 18

Use the information in the diagram to answer these questions:
a) Find the number of students scoring 18.
b) Find the number of students scoring 10-15 inclusive.
c) Find the number of students scoring 28 or more:
d) Find the highest score.
e) Find the modal score.
f) Find the mean score.
g) Find the median score.

 If you've got class-widths of 5, you ADD the numbers TOGETHER.

Q3 I did a survey to find out how many living relatives my friends have. Here are my results:

37 23 48 21 33 39
8 31 11 41 50 7
22 18 15 26 29 13

Draw a stem and leaf diagram to represent this data.
Use this key:

Key: 1 | 4   means 14

Q4 Use the information from this line graph to create your own stem and leaf diagram, using class-widths of 5. Then make a key to show how to use your diagram.

```
40 |
35 |
30 |
25 |
20 |
```

Key: | means

Frequency — Weight of 8 year olds (in kg)

Pie Charts

Everyone loves a pie chart. Oh, no, sorry, that's pies...

When constructing a pie chart, follow the three steps:

1) Add up the numbers in each sector to get the <u>TOTAL</u>.
2) Divide 360° by the <u>TOTAL</u> to get the <u>MULTIPLIER</u>.
3) Multiply <u>EVERY</u> number by the <u>MULTIPLIER</u> to get the <u>ANGLE</u> of each <u>SECTOR</u>.

Q1 A company that makes and sells pies wants to add a nutritional information diagram to their packaging. <u>Construct a pie chart</u> using the template on the right, to show the following nutritional data for one of their pies:

Contents of Pie	Amount per 100 g
Carbohydrate	35 g
Protein	15 g
Fat	10 g
Magical fairy dust	40 g

Q2 According to the tourist board for the Hindle Isles, 380,000 people visited the biggest island in the group, Sherrington, in 2009. The <u>distribution</u> of tourists for the <u>whole group of islands</u> is shown in the pie chart. Use a <u>protractor</u> on the diagram to find the number of tourists visiting the other islands in 2009 (rounded to the nearest 10,000).

Use the info you're given to find the number of tourists represented by 1°.

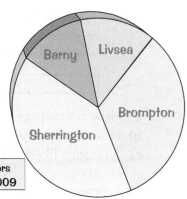

The distribution of visitors to the Hindle Isles in 2009

Q3 The pie chart shows the results of a survey of forty 11 year olds when asked what

their <u>favourite vegetable</u> is with Sunday lunch. Which one of the following may be <u>deduced</u> from the information in the <u>pie chart</u>?

a) Potatoes are the <u>least popular</u> vegetable.
b) 3/4 of the children <u>like potatoes</u> of some type.
c) 1/10 of the children like <u>carrots or cauliflower</u>.
d) 11/40 of the children asked what their favourite vegetable is, replied "<u>Don't eat vegetables</u>."

Q4 The pie charts opposite appear in a newspaper article about favourite pies. Nicki says that more women than men like apple pies.

Comment on <u>whether it's possible</u> to tell this from the pie charts.

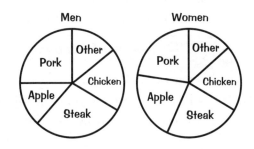

Other Graphs and Charts

 Make sure you read these questions carefully. You don't want to lose easy marks by looking at the wrong bit of the table or chart.

Q1 One hundred and sixty vehicles on a road were recorded as part of a traffic study. Complete the table and use it to answer the following questions.

a) How many cars were travelling north?
b) How many vans were travelling east?
c) How many trucks were travelling west?
d) How many motorbikes were recorded?

	Van	Motor-bike	Car	Truck	Total
Travelling North	3	2		5	
Travelling South	10			3	13
Travelling East			26	4	39
Travelling West	1		31		36
Total	21	7		13	160

Q2 This pictogram shows the favourite drinks of a group of pupils.

Favourite Drinks	Number of Pupils
Lemonade	✦ ✦ ✦ ✦ ✦ ✦ ✦ ✦ ✦
Cola	✦ ✦ ✦ ✦ ✦ ✦ ✦ ✦ ✦ ✦
Cherryade	✦ ✦ ✦ ✦ ✦ ⟨
Orange Squash	✦ ✦ ⟨
Milk	✦

✦ Represents 2 pupils.

a) How many pupils were questioned?
b) How many pupils prefer either milk or orange squash drinks?
c) 18 pupils liked lemonade best. How many more liked cola best? How many less liked cherryade best?
d) Comment on the popularity of cola compared with milk.

Q3 Carol was asked to find out if most people have a calculator in their Maths lessons. She asked the people she liked in her Maths set if they had brought a calculator to school. This table shows their responses:

Yes	No
II	III

From this she claims most people do not have a calculator.

a) Give 3 criticisms of Carol's survey.

Carol then conducts a more thorough survey. She asks what brand of calculator a student has and how much it cost. The results are shown in the tables below:

Brand	Awecalc	Functonne	Compbust	Numkorp	Pointswidge
Number	3	8	1	4	7

b) Is the brand data shown above discrete or continuous?
c) Plot a bar chart to show this data.

Other Graphs and Charts

Q4 A town council are planning to improve local sports facilities for children in the area. They asked a group of children which sport they preferred to play. The results are shown here:

Number of children	12	17	20	8	15
Type of Game	Basketball	Hockey	Rounders	Football	Tennis

a) Display this information as a frequency polygon.
b) How many children were surveyed?
c) How many more said they preferred Hockey than preferred Football?
d) Which sport should the council focus on improving the facilities for? Explain why.

Q5 The grading for skiers to be awarded certificates is as follows:
B - beginner, I - intermediate, G - good, VG - very good, R - racer.

To clarify the situation for a school group travelling to the Alps, the ski company would like a table and a chart to show the information as clearly as possible.
a) What sort of table can you suggest? Draw it accurately.
b) What sort of chart can you suggest? Draw it accurately.
c) What is the most common type of skier?

B	I	B	I	R	VG	I
I	R	G	VG	VG	B	B
I	I	B	B	R	B	G
I	B	G	G	I	I	I

Q6 Having seen the line graph opposite, a Quality Control Manager said "Admittedly we do have some complaints about our products, but from July complaints have tailed off, so our products must be of a better quality."
From the graph, do you think this statement is correct? Why/Why not?

Probability

Probability can be a bit of a struggle — here's a quick reminder of the basics...

PROBABILITIES are always between 0 and 1

1) You should express probabilities as a <u>fraction</u> or a <u>decimal</u>.
2) A probability of <u>ZERO</u> means that it will <u>definitely not</u> happen.
3) A probability of <u>ONE</u> means it will <u>definitely</u> happen.

Q1 The number line opposite is a <u>probability scale</u>. Place the letters where you think the following statements lie, in terms of the <u>chance</u> of the event happening.

   0   ½   1

a) The probability of getting a <u>head</u> on a toss of a 10p piece.
b) The probability of <u>choosing a red ball</u> from a bag containing 2 red balls and 1 green ball.
c) The probability of shaking a <u>five</u> on an ordinary dice.
d) The probability of choosing a <u>Guatemalan stamp</u> from a bag containing 60 British stamps and 40 French stamps.

Q2 Debbie's employer organises a weekly prize draw, where the winning employee is selected at random. Debbie only joins in if her chance of winning is at least 0.1. If there are 8 other people playing this week, will Debbie choose to play?

SHORTHAND NOTATION

1) <u>P(x) = 0.25</u> simply means "<u>the probability of event x happening is 0.25</u>".
2) E.g.: if you roll a dice, the <u>probability of rolling a 6</u> will be written as <u>P(rolls a 6)</u>.

Q3 After <u>49 tosses</u> of an unbiased coin, 24 have been heads and 25 have been tails. What is <u>P(50th toss will be a head)</u>?

Q4 If the probability of picking a banana from a fruit bowl is <u>0.27</u>, what is the probability of picking something which is <u>not</u> a banana?

Q5 A bag contains <u>3 red</u> balls, <u>4 blue</u> balls and <u>5 green</u> balls. A ball is chosen at random from the bag. What is the probability that:
a) it is green   c) it is red
b) it is blue   d) it is <u>not</u> red?

Q6 Students at school conduct a survey of the <u>colours</u> of parents' cars, where every parent owns one car. The table shows the results.

Red	Blue	Yellow	White	Green	Other
40	29	13	20	16	14

a) What is the probability of a parent owning a <u>red</u> car?
b) What is the probability of a parent owning a car that is <u>not</u> blue <u>or</u> green?

Probability

Q7 The probability of it raining during the monsoon is ¾, on a particular day.

a) What is the probability of it <u>not raining</u>?
b) If a monsoon 'season' lasts approximately <u>100 days</u>, how many days are likely to be <u>dry</u>?

Q8 Charlton is making a bet with his friend before the local cricket team play a match. He thinks the match will end in a draw. A local newspaper prints the team's results over their last 20 matches, as shown.

| W | W | L | D | D | W | W | L | W | L |
| D | L | L | D | W | D | W | W | L | L |

a) Complete the frequency table.

b) Charlton reasons that since there are 3 possible results for any match, the probability that the next match will be drawn (D) is $\frac{1}{3}$. Explain why Charlton is wrong.

Outcome	Frequency
W	
D	
L	

c) Suggest a value for the probability of a draw based on the team's past performance.

d) Based on their past performance, are the team most likely to win, lose, or draw?

Q9 a) What is the probability of randomly selecting either a black Ace or black King from an ordinary pack of playing cards?

Remember the OR rule — P(A or B) = P(A) + P(B).

b) If the entire suit of clubs is removed from a pack of cards, what is the probability of randomly selecting a red 7 from the remaining cards?

c) If all the 7s are also removed from the pack of cards, what is the probability of randomly selecting the 4 of diamonds?

Q10 For the spinner shown, the probability of landing on each of the numbers is listed in the table below.

Number	1	2	3	4	5	6
Probability	⅙	⅓	⅙	¹⁄₁₂	¹⁄₁₂	⅙

a) Find the probability of landing on an even number.

b) What is the probability of landing on black?

c) Why is the probability of landing on a white or a 3 not $\frac{5}{12} + \frac{1}{6}$?

Probability

Q11 The notepad below shows orders for 4 different sorts of rice at a certain Indian restaurant. Based on this data, what is the probability that the next order of rice is:

a) for pilau rice?

b) for spicy mushroom or special fried rice?

c) not for boiled rice?

If you're asked to work out probabilities based on some data, it's a <u>relative frequency</u> question.

boiled	20
pilau	24
spicy mushroom	10
special fried	6

Q12 a) A biased dice was rolled 40 times. A six came up 14 times. Calculate the relative frequency of rolling a six.

b) In a different experiment the same dice was rolled 60 times. A six came up 24 times. Calculate the relative frequency of rolling a six based on the second experiment.

c) Use the data from a) and b) to make the best estimate you can of the probability of rolling a six with this dice.

Q13 a) A 20-sided dice is rolled 150 times. A one came up 13 times. Calculate the relative frequency of rolling a one.

b) A 12-sided dice is rolled 80 times. A five came up 4 times. Calculate the relative frequency of rolling a five.

c) Two 10-sided dice were rolled together 250 times. One was green and the other was red. Three came up on the green dice 23 times. Ten came up on the red dice 33 times. One these dice is biased. Explain which one you think it is and why.

Q14 There are 2 spinners: one with 3 sides numbered 1, 2, 3, and the other with 7 sides numbered 1, 2, 3, 4, 5, 6, 7.

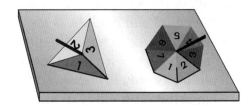

a) If both are spun together, list all the possible outcomes.

b) Complete the following table showing the sum of the 2 numbers for each outcome.

	1	2	3	4	5	6	7
1							
2							
3							

c) What is the probability that the sum is 6?

d) What is the probability that the sum is even?

e) What is the probability that the sum is greater than or equal to 8?

f) What is the probability that the sum is less than 8?

g) Explain how you can work out the probability in part **f)** without using the table.

Probability

Q15 Kenny has written a random number generating computer program, Numbertron 5000.
He thinks a bug has made the program biased towards odd numbers.
He tests it by making it pick a number from 1 to 10. He does this 80 times.
If the program is really random, how many times in 80 trials would you expect it to pick:

a) 4?   **b)** an odd number?

Here are the results of Kenny's experiment:

Number	1	2	3	4	5	6	7	8	9	10
No. of times picked	7	7	9	8	10	7	9	6	8	9

c) What is the relative frequency of Numbertron 5000 picking an odd number?

d) If the program is truly random, what would you expect to happen to the relative
frequency of each number if Kenny repeated the experiment with 100 000 trials?

Q16 3 balls are drawn at random, without replacement, from a
bag containing 4 green balls and 3 red balls.

a) Complete the tree diagram below showing all the possible
outcomes and their probabilities.

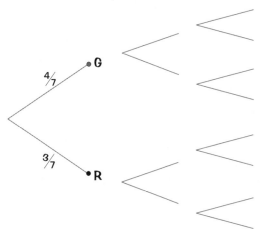

For AND you MULTIPLY along the branches.
For OR you ADD the end results.

b) What is the probability that exactly 2 green balls are drawn?
c) What is the probability that the last ball drawn is the same
colour as the first?

Q17 A box contains 6 tabby cats, 3 black cats and 4 Siamese cats. There is a hole in the box
which is only big enough for one cat to walk through at a time. The cats never walk back
into the box. Use a tree diagram to work out the probability that:

a) the first two cats to leave the box are both Siamese
b) if three cats leave the box at least one of them will be black
c) the first three cats to leave the box will be of different types
d) the first three cats will be a Siamese, a tabby and a black cat in that order.

Probability

Q18 How many times must you roll an ordinary 6-sided dice for the probability of getting at least one 6 to be more than 0.5?

Don't forget the "at least" trick —
P(at least 1 six) = 1 – P(no sixes).

Q19 An unbiased dice in the shape of a tetrahedron has faces numbered 1, 2, 3, 4.
To win a game with this dice, you must throw a 4.
On each turn you have a maximum of 3 attempts.

a) Using a tree diagram, calculate the probability of winning
with the second throw of your first turn.

b) What is the probability of winning on the first go?

Q20 3 coins are drawn at random, without replacement, from a piggy bank containing
7 pound coins and 4 twenty-pence pieces.

a) Draw a tree diagram showing all possible outcomes and their probabilities.

b) Find the probability that the first coin selected is different in value from the third.

c) Find the probability that less than £1.50 is drawn altogether.

Q21 Fabrizio is practising taking penalties. The probability that he misses the goal completely
is $\frac{1}{8}$. The probability that the goalkeeper saves the penalty is $\frac{3}{8}$. The probability that he
scores is $\frac{1}{2}$. Fabrizio takes two penalties.

a) Calculate the probability that Fabrizio fails to score with his two penalties.

b) Calculate the probability that he scores only one goal.

c) Calculate the probability that Fabrizio scores on neither or both of his 2 attempts.

Q22 Trevor and his 2 brothers and 5 friends are seated at random in a row of 8 seats at the
cinema. What is the probability that Trevor has one brother on his immediate left and
one on his immediate right?

Careful here — you have to include the probability
that Trevor sits in one of the six middle seats.

Drawing a tree diagram might be a bit of a faff, but it can really help to make
the question clearer. So if you're stuck, give the old tree diagram a try.